Contents

01
Health and safety law

Contents

Supporting information

GT 700 Toolbox talks

A 01

Overview

The purpose of health and safety legislation is to protect the wellbeing of those at work and others, such as the general public, by ensuring work is carried out in a manner that is safe and free of risks to health for everyone who may be affected.

There are a number of different legislative requirements that must be followed to ensure this is achieved. This chapter outlines the main Act and regulations that apply.

1.1 Introduction

There have always been accidents and ill health resulting from people carrying out work. Fortunately, we have come a long way from earlier days when such events were simply accepted as part of having a job – many people went to work and took their chances. Even so, workplace accidents and work-related ill health still occur, with the building and construction industry having a disproportionately high rate of both.

Everyone who goes to work has a right to return home uninjured and in a good state of health. Similarly, visitors to sites and passers-by have the same right to the protection of their health and safety.

When health and safety law is broken, a criminal offence is committed. If the results are sufficiently serious the offence can be punishable by a fine or even imprisonment. Less serious breaches of health and safety law can result in an enforcement or improvement notice being issued, or simply advice being offered.

Whilst health and safety legislation is embedded in criminal law, in some circumstances legislation gives a person who has been injured or made ill through work the right to take legal action against the employer for compensation, through the civil courts.

You can insure against civil liabilities but you cannot insure against criminal liabilities.

The primary focus of health and safety legislation is to put legal duties on employers (and the self-employed, who in many cases have the same legal duties as employers) to ensure that work is carried out safely and without risks to health.

It should be noted that some legislation places legal duties upon employees. In specific situations, legal duties are also placed upon *duty holders*, as defined in the relevant legislation. The actions that must be taken to fulfil these duties are explained in the appropriate chapters of this book.

In many situations, site-based staff (such as supervisors, site managers or project managers) will be nominated by the employer to ensure that the employer's legal duties are complied with at site level. However, legal duties still lie with the employer who must be confident in the ability and competence of their supervisors, managers and others who manage health and safety on their behalf.

1.2 History of health and safety law

Since the introduction of the Health and Safety at Work etc. Act (HSAW) in 1974, Britain is achieving one of the best health and safety records in the world. In 1974 there were 651 fatalities to employees. In 2013-14 this figure was down to 133 for employees and the self-employed. This is a reduction of 85% over the past 40 years. Injuries at work have reduced over the same period, from 336,701 down to 78,222. A significant reduction can also be seen in the number of construction industry fatality rates. In 1974 there were over 150 fatalities, whereas in 2013-14 there were 42 fatalities. The graph below shows the number of fatal injuries to employees (RIDDOR) from 1974 to 2013.

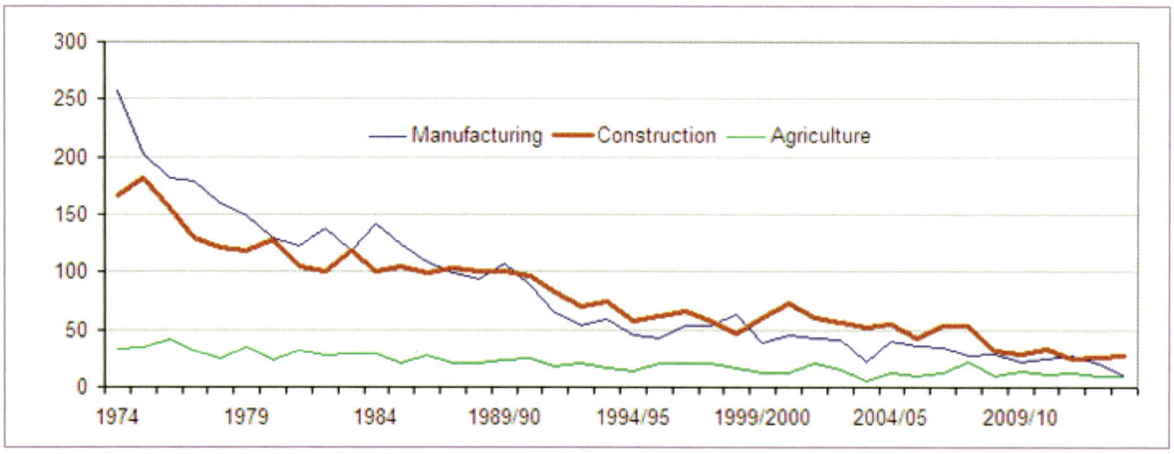

(Source: HSE)

These figures are still too high and the industry remains a high risk for injuries, but the significant improvements are evident. An example of this is the delivery of the London 2012 Olympic Games. On this project there were no work-related fatalities during the work to build the new venues or during the staging of the games.

Before the introduction of the 1974 Act there were a number of different regulations or, in some areas, there were no regulations at all. The HSWA became an enabling Act and since its introduction it has allowed for a number of regulations to be implemented and subsequently revised and/or revoked where necessary.

Forty years on the HSWA has demonstrated it can be applied to new responsibilities and demands, creating the framework for people to come home safe and well from a day's work in any sector of the economy. *(For further information on the HSWA refer to 1.5.)*

- ☑ The first Act of Parliament directly concerned with safety was the Factories Act, passed in 1802, which dealt with the morals of apprentices.
- ☑ From 1812 onwards, a succession of Acts regulated working conditions in factories, with particular reference to women and children.
- ☑ In 1833, the first four factory inspectors were appointed. Children aged nine were being sent up chimneys as chimney sweeps, where they could work a 48-hour week. They were supposed to spend two hours a day at school. People as young as 13 sometimes worked a 69-hour week.
- ☑ The first two female factory inspectors were appointed in 1893 and the first medical inspector in 1898.
- ☑ In 1901, a comprehensive Factories and Workshops Act was passed. It lasted until the Factories Act of 1937 replaced it, then this, in turn, was repealed by the Factories Act of 1961.
- ☑ The Health and Safety at Work Act, the basis for modern legislation, came into force in 1974, bringing with it protection for virtually everyone at work and consolidating much of the earlier industry-specific legislation under a single Act.
- ☑ The Construction (Design and Management) (CDM) Regulations 1994 were drafted to address the continuing unacceptably high rate of accidents and ill health befalling construction workers.
- ☑ In 2005 the Working at Height Regulations were introduced to prevent death and injury caused by falls from height. The regulations require employers and those in control of any work at height to ensure that work is properly planned, supervised and carried out by competent workers.
- ☑ The CDM Regulations were revised in 2007 and are the cornerstone legislation for the construction industry. They reinforced the requirements for competence, co-operation and co-ordination, with a focus on 'the right information, to the right people, at the right time'.
- ☑ The coming into force of the Corporate Manslaughter and Corporate Homicide Act and the Health and Safety (Offences) Act, demonstrate a hardening of Government's attitude towards serious breaches of health and safety legislation.
- ☑ The Löfstedt report *Reclaiming health and safety for all: an independent review of health and safety legislation* was published in 2011 as part of the Government's plan to overhaul the health and safety system in Britain. The report considers how legislation can be combined and simplified, aiming to reduce the burden on British businesses, which has resulted in a review of current legislation, including CDM.
- ☑ In 2012 the Control of Asbestos Regulations came into force. This updated the earlier asbestos regulations and made changes around some types of non-licensed work with asbestos, including medical surveillance, record keeping and notification of work.
- ☑ The Health and Safety (Fees) Regulations (introduced in 2012) administer the Health and Safety Executive (HSE) cost recovery scheme. HSE recoup their costs against those who contravene health and safety laws.
- ☑ In 2015 the CDM Regulations were amended to implement the requirements of Directive 92/57/EEC. The main changes are to make the regulations easier to understand, replace the CDM co-ordinator role with a principal designer, replace the detailed and prescriptive requirements for individual and corporate competence with a more generic requirement, and align notification requirements with the Directive and apply the regulations to domestic clients in a proportionate way.

1.3 Summary of health and safety law

Health and safety law

Common law
(Duty of care)

Statute law
(Written)

Types of statutory duty

Absolute duty	Practicable	Reasonably practicable

Health and Safety at Work Act 1974

The Act consists of four parts

Part 1. Health and safety of people at work and protection of others who may be affected
Part 2. Employment Medical Advisory Service
Part 3. Amends to previous law
Part 4. General and miscellaneous provisions

General duties for employers and employees

Health and safety regulations

Regulations require additional specific actions

They can be concerning:

- health and safety management
- workplaces and dangerous substances
- machinery, handling and equipment
- specific areas of work or situations

ACoPs Approved Codes of Practice

ACoPs explain what measures must be taken to comply with relevant regulations

Following an ACoP (or an equivalent standard) is generally accepted as being legally compliant

Industry guidance

Industry guidance notes

Issued by the HSE and give practical guidance on how regulations may be complied with

Industry guidance

Practical guidance produced by industry associations, federations and training bodies

1.4 Contract, common and statute law

All employers, principal contractors, contractors and the self-employed, as well as employees, can have responsibilities in three distinct areas of law.

1.4.1 Contract law

- ☑ Agreement by two parties.
- ☑ Both parties must intend to form a legally binding agreement, and must have the authority to enter into the contract.
- ☑ Under the Contracts (Right of Third Parties) Act the contract can include or exclude the rights of a third person.

1.4.2 Common law

- ☑ Evolved over centuries with judicial judgements creating binding precedents.
- ☑ Decisions made in higher courts are binding on all lower courts.
- ☑ Where parties disagree on the law, a common law court looks to past precedential decisions of relevant courts. If a similar dispute has been resolved in the past, the court is bound to follow the reasoning used in the prior decision.
- ☑ If the current dispute is fundamentally distinct from all previous cases judges have the authority and duty to make law by creating a new precedent.
- ☑ An individual has the right to protection from harm and the right to sue for compensation when they suffer loss, ill health, or injury through the negligence of another.

1.4.3 Statute law

- ☑ Acts of Parliament, regulations and EU Directives.
- ☑ Laws made by the government.
- ☑ The Health and Safety at Work Act is an enabling act, which permits the Secretary of State or other ministers to replace legislation with regulations requiring a higher standard of health and safety.
- ☑ Regulations are referred to as statutory instruments that are made under the enabling act.

1.5 Health and Safety at Work Act 1974

The Health and Safety at Work Act 1974 is the primary piece of health and safety legislation in the United Kingdom. The Act is termed as an enabling Act, which allows the Government to make health and safety regulations that become part of the law. The requirements of the Act are very general and wide-ranging, such as:

> **It shall be the duty of every employer to ensure, so far as is reasonably practicable, the health, safety and welfare at work of all their employees.**

This typical requirement does not specify any technical requirements or set any minimum standards of behaviour that can be measured, but it does clearly outline the requirement for safe places of work.

Health and safety regulations expand upon the legal requirements of the Act with regard to specific occupational work and include specific and technical requirements. Health and safety regulations are often supported by guidance notes or Approved Codes of Practice (ACoPs), which explain in plain language how compliance with the law can be achieved.

The Act is covered in Chapter A02 The Health and Safety at Work Act.

The legal duties of employers and employees, as specified in the Health and Safety at Work Act 1974 are shown below.

1.5.1 Employers' responsibilities

An employer must, so far as is reasonably practicable:

- ☑ protect the health, safety and welfare at work of all their employees
- ☑ provide and maintain plant and systems of work that are safe and without risk to health
- ☑ have arrangements for ensuring safety and absence of risk to health in connection with the use, handling, storage and transport of articles and substances
- ☑ provide such information, instruction, training and supervision as is necessary to ensure the health and safety at work of employees
- ☑ maintain any place of work under their control in a condition that is safe and without risks to health, and with access to and egress from it, that are safe and without such risks
- ☑ provide and maintain a working environment that is safe, without risks to health and adequate as regards the welfare of employees.

1.5.2 Employees' duties

- ☑ Take reasonable care for the health and safety of themselves or others who may be affected by their acts or omissions.
- ☑ Co-operate with their employer in all matters relating to health and safety.
- ☑ Not intentionally or recklessly interfere with or misuse anything provided in the interests of health, safety and welfare.
- ☑ Use anything provided by the employer in accordance with instructions.
- ☑ Report anything that is thought to be dangerous.

The requirement, on the employer, to do what is reasonably practicable to ensure the health, safety and welfare of employees at work is balanced by a requirement, on the employees, to comply with any necessary rules or instructions and to take reasonable care of themselves and others.

1.6 Health and safety regulations

Many sets of regulations have been developed and introduced as a means of incorporating European Union legislation into our domestic legal framework. There are many sets of health and safety regulations in existence that are relevant to the work carried out by the construction industry. Some sets of regulations apply to construction work only.

Health and safety regulations are a part of UK law that place duties on employers and employees. It is a criminal offence to contravene them. Some examples of legislation that affect the building and construction industry are shown below.

1.6.1 Construction (Design and Management) Regulations

The main aim is to ensure that health and safety risks are considered and addressed, from concept through to completion of the project. The guidance identifies the main elements to securing construction health and safety, as shown below.

- ☑ Applying the **general principles of prevention**.
- ☑ **Appointing** the right people and organisations at the right time.
- ☑ Ensuring everyone has the **information, instruction, training and supervision** necessary to enable them to carry out their jobs in a way that secures health and safety.
- ☑ Duty holders **co-operating and communicating** with each other and **co-ordinating** their work.
- ☑ **Consulting workers and engaging** with them to promote and develop effective measures to secure health, safety and welfare.

1.6.2 Control of Asbestos Regulations

Requires identifying asbestos-containing materials (ACMs) before any work is carried out.

1.6.3 Electricity at Work Regulations

People in control of electrical systems must ensure that they are safe to use and they are maintained in a safe condition.

1.6.4 Health and Safety (Display Screen Equipment) Regulations

Aims to protect the health of people who work with display screen equipment. These regulations were introduced because display screen equipment has become one of the most common kinds of work equipment. Incorrect use of display screen equipment (DSE) can result in upper limb disorders and other conditions, such as repetitive strain injury (RSI).

The following legal duties are placed on employers.

- ☑ Analyse the workstation to assess or reduce risk.
- ☑ Make sure controls are in place.
- ☑ Provide information and training.
- ☑ Provide eyesight tests, on request.
- ☑ Review the DSE assessment when the user or DSE changes.

1.6.5 Management of Health and Safety at Work Regulations

This regulation makes employers' duties more explicit and explains what they need to do to manage health and safety. The main requirement is for employers to carry out a suitable and sufficient risk assessment. (The duty to risk assess includes the duty to identify specific risks to young people and new and expectant mothers.) Employers with five or more employees need to record significant findings of the risk assessment.

1.6.6 Provision and Use of Work Equipment Regulations

Correct equipment must be provided, inspected, tested and properly maintained.

1.6.7 Reporting of Injuries, Diseases and Dangerous Occurrences Regulations (RIDDOR)

A legal duty is placed on employers, the self-employed and those in control of premises to report:

- ☑ work-related deaths or specified injuries
- ☑ injuries resulting in an absence of more than seven days
- ☑ reportable diseases
- ☑ dangerous occurrences.

1.6.8 Work at Height Regulations

Duty holders are required to ensure the following.

- ☑ All work at height is properly planned and organised.
- ☑ All work at height takes account of weather conditions that could endanger health and safety.
- ☑ Those involved in work at height are trained and competent.
- ☑ The place where work at height is carried out is safe.
- ☑ Equipment for work at height is appropriately inspected.
- ☑ The risks from fragile surfaces are properly controlled, as are the risks from falling objects.

1.6.9 Working Time Regulations

Implements the European Working Time Directive and governs the hours most workers can work. The following are specified in the regulations.

- ☑ Set limits on the average working week, to 48 hours per week over a 17-week period.
- ☑ Statutory entitlement to paid leave for most workers.
- ☑ Limit the normal hours of night work.
- ☑ Limit the working time of young people to not exceed eight hours a day, or 40 hours a week.
- ☑ Allow a daily rest period of 11 hours between each working day, and a weekly rest period of not less than 24 hours in each seven day period, but this may be averaged over two weeks.
- ☑ Entitle an adult worker to a rest break of not less than 20 minutes, within a daily working time of more than six hours.
- ☑ Entitle a young person to a rest break of at least 30 minutes, when they are working more than four and a half hours.

1.6.10 Workplace (Health, Safety and Welfare) Regulations

This regulation covers a wide range of basic health, safety and welfare issues and applies to most workplaces, with the exception of workplaces involving construction work on construction sites. The requirements of these regulations are covered by the Work at Height Regulations and the Construction (Design and Management) Regulations.

1.7 Approved Codes of Practice

The Health and Safety at Work Act 1974 makes provision for the production of ACoPs, where appropriate, in support of some health and safety regulations.

Approved Codes of Practice are prepared and issued by the HSE and are often referred to as ACoPs.

Whilst not strictly a part of the law, ACoPs have special legal status in that failure to comply with the guidance contained in an ACoP may be cited in court as a failure to comply with the law and may form part of the evidence in a health and safety prosecution. ACoPs explain in detail what measures must be taken to comply with the regulations to which the ACoP relates.

Where an employer is accused of failing to comply with the requirements of an ACoP it is a valid defence for the employer if it can be shown that alternative measures, which were equally or more effective, were implemented.

ACoPs are generally issued after wide public consultation with stakeholders, the involvement of other Government bodies and with the consent of the Secretary of State.

1.8 Guidance notes

These are issued by the HSE and give practical advice on how regulations may be complied with.

While they are not legally enforceable, they do provide practical guidance on how employers and employees may comply with health and safety legislation.

A
01

1.9 Standards of compliance

Within health and safety legislation specific words or phrases are used to qualify or describe the standard of compliance that must be achieved with regard to some legal duties, such as the words absolute, practicable (or best practicable means) or reasonably practicable. The meanings of these are explained below.

1.9.1 It shall be the duty of an employer to...

This means that the employer **must** comply with the legal duty being described, regardless of time, effort and cost. The word 'shall' (if not qualified by the phrase 'so far as reasonably practicable' or the word 'practicable') leaves no scope for not complying with the duty. This can also be referred to as an **absolute** duty.

1.9.2 It shall be the duty of an employer to... as far as is practicable

'Practicable' means that there is no scope for taking cost and convenience into account; the duty must be complied with if it is possible to carry it out within the current state of knowledge and technology (if it is technically possible, then the duty must be complied with).

e.g. **Practicable**

It was necessary for someone to use a disc cutter to cut paving slabs to the required size.

The legal duty requires that the rotating blade of the machine be guarded to the extent that it is practicable to do so. This acknowledges that total guarding of the blade is not possible because the machine could not then be used for the job for which it was designed.

The law requires that the guard be adjusted to expose enough blade to enable the job to be carried out safely whilst providing the maximum degree of protection for the operator.

Not to use a guard at all is not an option, even if it causes cost or inconvenience.

1.9.3 It shall be the duty of an employer to... as far as is reasonably practicable

Where a requirement to carry out a specific legal duty is qualified by the phrase 'as far as is reasonably practicable', employers are allowed to exercise their judgement on the extent of the measures that need to be taken to ensure the health and safety of the person(s) carrying out the job and anyone else who may be affected by it.

Deciding what are reasonably practicable measures to take should be based upon the findings of a risk assessment.

Reasonably practicable **means that the risks involved in carrying out the work may be balanced against the cost in terms of money, inconvenience and time.**

Where the risks to health and safety in carrying out a job are found to be low in comparison to what would be disproportionately high costs to totally overcome the risks, the employer need only take the measures that are considered to be reasonably practicable.

e.g. **Reasonably practicable**

It was necessary to provide access to working platforms of a scaffold at four different levels for a 12-week period, the higher level being a narrow lift between two structures. A decision had to be made on the best means of access.

Legislation on working at height requires 'every employer to ensure that work at height is carried out in a manner which is, so far as reasonably practicable, safe'.

In planning the job, the risk assessment showed:

- ☑ it would be necessary for tools and materials for various trades to be carried up to and down from the main working platform but not from the higher level lift. The ground was firm and level and there was plenty of space at the bottom of the scaffold
- ☑ if a ladder was used, it could be securely tied to the scaffold and suitable handholds could be provided at the stepping-off point. The tools and materials would have to be hoisted up using a small electric hoist fixed to the scaffold
- ☑ various trades could be working together and at the same time only one means of access was required, not a place of work, to the higher level lift. There were no weather considerations that would make the use of a ladder unduly unsafe.

Given the circumstances, it was decided that a ladder was not a reasonably practicable measure to prevent a fall with regard to access to the main working platform where tools and materials were required and therefore a stair tower was used. For access to the higher level lift a ladder was considered to be suitable, complete with a ladder safety gate. The stair tower also offered quicker, safer and easier access.

1.9.4 Burden of proof

Many of the duties on employers are qualified with the phrases 'so far as is reasonably practicable' or 'so far as is practicable'.

Generally, in a court of law a defendant is innocent until proven guilty. However, with regard to these phrases, the burden of proof is reversed and so the defendant must prove that it was not reasonably practicable, or practicable, as the case may be, to do more than was done to mitigate the risks. In effect, the defendant is guilty until they prove their innocence.

1.10 Consultation

The HSWA made provisions for the appointment of a safety representative from a recognised trade union (Regulation 2(4)) and as a result the **Safety Representatives and Safety Committees Regulations** were introduced. This regulation applies on sites where an employee is a member of a recognised trade union.

Regulation 14 of the CDM Regulations requires the principal contractor to consult and engage with workers. Their duties include making arrangements to ensure workers co-operate, consulting with workers or representatives in good time on matters relating to health and safety and ensuring workers or their representative can inspect or take copies of any information that may affect health, safety and welfare on site.

www.

For examples of how the principal contractor could consult with workers refer to the CDM industry guidance for workers.

The aim of all applicable regulations is to promote effective two-way dialogue between employers and employees, or their representatives.

On sites where there is no recognised trade union member representation the **Health and Safety (Consultation with Employee) Regulations** will apply. These regulations were introduced as the HSWA only covers union-appointed safety representatives. This regulation gives all employees, whether union-appointed or not, the right to have consultation with their employers and to be provided with information. There are many similarities with the Safety Representatives and Safety Committee Regulations.

The following areas are covered by the regulations.

- ☑ Duty of the employer to consult.
- ☑ Persons to be consulted.
- ☑ Provision of information.
- ☑ Functions of the representative of employee safety.
- ☑ Training, time off and the provision of facilities.

1.10.1 Duty of the employer to consult

It is the duty of the employer to consult with their employees in good time on the following types of health and safety measures.

- ☑ The introduction of any measures that will affect the health and safety of employees.
- ☑ The arrangements for appointing or nominating the person(s) to assist the employer in complying with health and safety legislation.
- ☑ The provision of relevant information as required under health and safety legislation.
- ☑ Any planning or organisation of training required by relevant health and safety legislation.
- ☑ The health and safety implications of the introduction of new technologies into the employer's workplace.

1.10.2 Persons to be consulted

Employers may consult directly with all their employees or through representatives of employee safety, elected by a group of employees to represent them in health and safety consultation with their employer.

The employer must provide employees with a list of names of representatives of employee safety and the group they are representing in the workplace. The employer must inform employees of any changes in the form of consultation, such as a move from dealing with representatives to directly consulting with each employee. The employee representatives must also inform the employer when they no longer represent a group or groups of employees.

1.10.3 Provision of information

The employer must provide any information that the employees may require in order for them to participate fully in the consultation procedure. This will either be directly with all employees or with the elected representatives of employee safety.

The following are issues that the employer must consult on.

- ☑ Introduction of measures at the workplace that may substantially affect the health and safety of employees.
- ☑ Arrangements for obtaining or appointing the competent person to assist the employer to comply with health and safety requirements.
- ☑ Information on risks to employees' health and safety and the measures taken to remove or minimise them.

1.10.4 Functions of the representatives of employee safety

The functions of the representatives of employee safety are similar to those of the trade union safety representative appointed under the Safety Representatives and Safety Committee Regulations. They may make representations on hazards, risks, dangerous occurrences, ill health and general health and safety matters.

1.10.5 Training, time off and provision of facilities

The employer must provide the employee representative with appropriate and reasonable training time and reasonable facilities to enable them to perform their functions. This includes the employer meeting reasonable costs associated with training and time off to perform the function. The employee is protected from unfair dismissal when participating in consultation with employers on matters.

1.11 Occupiers' Liability Act

Legal duties are placed on the occupiers of premises to ensure the health and safety of anyone entering those premises, whether authorised to be there or not.

- ☑ The Occupiers' Liability Act covers civil law duties that an occupier of any land or premises has towards other people in general.
- ☑ It applies irrespective of whether the owner is the occupier or the premises are rented or occupied under any terms.
- ☑ Where premises, or part of the premises, are handed over to the contractor, it would be likely that the contractor would be regarded as the occupier.
- ☑ Premises include the grounds surrounding a building (for example, an unfenced excavation outside a construction site).
- ☑ A visitor can be anyone who is not an employee. Therefore a visitor may be any person who is a lawful visitor with genuine reason to visit the premises, or a trespasser.
- ☑ The occupier must expect children and young persons to be inquisitive to trespass. Therefore greater measures may be required where the risk is foreseeable.
- ☑ Control measures (such as immobilising plant and machinery, isolating sources of ignition, locking away substances hazardous to health, providing lighting and correct stacking of materials) should be implemented, where applicable.

One area of particular concern is house building or work in the repairs and maintenance industry, when property may remain in occupation at the time of the work being undertaken. Additional control measures may be required if the work areas cannot be fully segregated from other persons in the premises.

1.12 Corporate Manslaughter and Corporate Homicide Act

Since 6 April 2008, companies whose gross negligence leads to the death of individuals can face prosecution for manslaughter (homicide in Scotland) under the Corporate Manslaughter and Corporate Homicide Act.

Under this legislation companies, organisations and, for the first time, Government bodies face an unlimited fine if they are found to have caused death due to their gross corporate health and safety failures. The legislation primarily came about as a result of the failure to identify 'the controlling mind' in companies with complex management structures during court cases, which followed several high profile disasters.

However, presentations by authoritative legal professionals have indicated that the legislation might have much wider ranging implications (such as prosecutions following at-work-related road deaths and fatalities).

The Act offers employees of companies, consumers and other individuals greater protection against corporate negligence. It will also focus the minds of those in companies and other organisations by ensuring that they take their health and safety obligations seriously.

1.12.1 Corporate Manslaughter Act

The Act applies to the whole of the United Kingdom, with the term *corporate homicide* applying to Scotland only.

The Corporate Manslaughter and Corporate Homicide Act:

- ☑ makes it easier to prosecute companies and other large organisations when gross failures in the management of health and safety lead to death by delivering a new, more effective basis for corporate liability
- ☑ has reformed the law so that an important obstacle to successful prosecutions has now been removed. It means that both small and large companies can be held liable for manslaughter where gross failures in the management of health and safety cause death, not just health and safety violations
- ☑ complements the current law under which individuals can be prosecuted for gross negligence manslaughter and health and safety offences, where there is direct evidence of their culpability. The Act builds on existing health and safety legislation – so the new offence does not impose new regulations on business
- ☑ lifts Crown immunity to prosecution. Crown bodies – such as Government departments – will be liable to prosecution for the first time. So the Act will apply to companies and other corporate bodies, in the public and private sector, Government departments, police forces and certain unincorporated bodies, such as partnerships, where these are employers.

(The above text is an extract reproduced from a Ministry of Justice press release under licence from Her Majesty's Stationery Office.)

An organisation will be guilty of the offence if someone has been killed as a result of the gross failure of an organisation's senior managers, for example, failure to ensure safe working practices for their employees (for example, staff are properly trained and equipment is in a safe condition) or maintain the safety of their premises (for example, ensuring that lifts are properly maintained and fire precautions taken).

The Act covers organisations providing goods and services to members of the public, the construction, use or maintenance of infrastructure or vehicles, or when operating commercially. Crown bodies and other public sector organisations, including police forces, will be on an equal footing with the private sector when carrying out similar work.

The offence is clearly linked to the standards required under other health and safety laws. It does not apply to circumstances where an organisation does not owe a duty of care or to certain public and government functions whose management involves wider questions of public policy and are already subject to other forms of accountability. For example, it does not apply to strategic decisions about the spending of public money or activities like statutory inspection, holding prisoners in detention, the response of the emergency services, policing or child protection.

If a company is found guilty of corporate manslaughter the penalty will be an unlimited fine. The Act also gives the courts power to impose a remedial order, which can already be imposed for health and safety offences, and requires the company to address the cause of the fatality.

1.12.2 Sentencing

In February 2010 the Sentencing Guidelines Council issued guidance to the courts regarding sentencing options under the Corporate Manslaughter and Corporate Homicide Act. Pertinent points in the guidelines are listed below.

- ☑ Fines for companies and organisations found guilty of corporate manslaughter may be millions of pounds and should seldom be below £500,000.
- ☑ Fines for other health and safety offences causing death should range from £100,000 to several hundreds of thousands of pounds.
- ☑ In deciding the level of fine, account must be taken of the financial circumstances of the offending organisation.
- ☑ When fixing a fine, a court should not be influenced by the impact on shareholders and directors, nor consider the costs of complying with other sanctions.
- ☑ Account may be taken of the effect on the employment of the innocent (employees), as may the effect on the delivery of services to the public.

Circumstances that courts should regard as aggravating factors include the following.

- ☑ The number of deaths.
- ☑ Injury to vulnerable persons.
- ☑ A failure to heed previous warnings or respond to near-misses of a similar nature.
- ☑ Cost-cutting (profits take priority over safety).
- ☑ Failure to obtain or comply with relevant licences.

1.13 Health and Safety (Offences) Act

The HSE has made it clear that its enforcement policy will be to target those who cut corners to gain a financial advantage over competitors, by failing to comply with health and safety law and therefore putting workers and others at risk.

This legislation, which came into force in January 2009, amends Section 33 of the Health and Safety at Work Act 1974, and in doing so it:

- ☑ increased the maximum fine that can be awarded by the courts for breaches of health and safety regulations, from £5,000 to £20,000
- ☑ increased the number of health and safety offences for which a guilty person can be imprisoned
- ☑ enables certain offences, which could previously only be tried in Magistrates' Courts, to be tried in either Magistrates' Courts or Crown Courts.

A
01

The table below summarises a new Schedule 3A to the Health and Safety at Work Act 1974; it sets out the offences and maximum penalties under health and safety legislation. The table lists those offences that are likely to be most relevant to employers and site management.

Offence	Court	Maximum penalty
A breach of Sections 2–6, which set out the general duties of employers, self-employed persons, persons who have control of premises, employees, manufacturers and suppliers to safeguard the health and safety of employees and members of the public who may be affected by work activities.	Lower court maximum	£20,000 fine and/or 12 months' imprisonment*
	Higher court maximum	Unlimited fine and/or two years' imprisonment
A breach of Section 7, which is the failure of an individual to take reasonable care of their own health and safety or that of someone else who is affected by their acts or omissions, or to co-operate with the employer in matters of health and safety.	Lower court maximum	£5,000 fine and/or 12 months' imprisonment*
	Higher court maximum	Unlimited fine and/or two years' imprisonment
A breach of Section 8, which imposes a duty on all persons not to intentionally or recklessly interfere with anything provided in the interests of health, safety or welfare.	Lower court maximum	£20,000 fine and/or 12 months' imprisonment*
	Higher court maximum	Unlimited fine and/or two years' imprisonment
A breach of Section 9, which imposes a duty on employers not to make a charge for anything provided in the interests of health or safety.	Lower court maximum	£20,000 fine
	Higher court maximum	Unlimited fine
A breach of Section 33(1)(c), which is to contravene any health and safety regulation.	Lower court maximum	£20,000 fine and/or 12 months' imprisonment
	Higher court maximum	Unlimited fine and/or two years' imprisonment
A breach of Sections 33(1) (e), (f) or (g), which are concerned with: ▪ contravening any requirement of an inspector when exercising their enforcement powers ▪ preventing anyone appearing before an inspector, or ▪ contravening any requirement imposed by an improvement or prohibition notice.	Lower court maximum	£20,000 fine and/or 12 months' imprisonment*
	Higher court maximum	Unlimited fine and/or two years' imprisonment
A breach of Section 33(1)(h), which is to intentionally obstruct an inspector in exercising their powers or duties.	Lower court maximum	£5,000 fine and/or 51 weeks' imprisonment** (12 months in Scotland)
	Higher court maximum	Not applicable
A breach of Sections 33(1)(k), (l) or (m), which are concerned with making false statements, false entries in a register or book or forging or using a document to deceive an inspector.	Lower court maximum	£20,000 fine and/or 12 months' imprisonment*
	Higher court maximum	Unlimited fine and/or two years' imprisonment
A breach of Section 33(1)(o), which is to fail to comply with a court remedy order under Section 42.	Lower court maximum	£20,000 fine and/or 12 months' imprisonment*
	Higher court maximum	Unlimited fine and/or two years' imprisonment
A breach of Sections 36 or 37 of HSW Act, which relate to offences committed by corporate bodies due to the personal failings of directors, senior managers, company secretaries, and so on. *See also Note 4 below.*	Lower court maximum	Five years' disqualification
	Higher court maximum	15 years' disqualification

Notes

1. *A lower court is a Magistrate's Court (or Sheriff's Court in Scotland).*
2. *A higher court is a Crown Court (or High Court of Judiciary in Scotland).*
3. **The powers of Magistrates' Courts to award prison sentences of 12 months will not come into force until Section 154(1) of the Criminal Justice Act comes into force and should be read as six months' imprisonment until that time.*
   ***Similarly, the reference to a 51-week prison sentence will not come into force until Section 281(5) of the Criminal Justice Act comes into force and should be read as six months' imprisonment until that time.*
4. *On conviction of directors for indictable offences in connection with the management of a company, the courts may also make a disqualification order (Company Directors Disqualification Act 1986, Sections 1 and 2). The courts have exercised this power following health and safety convictions and health and safety inspectors draw this power to the court's attention whenever appropriate.*

02

The Health and Safety at Work Act

Contents

Supporting information

G: Checklists and forms

GT 700 Toolbox talks

Overview

The Health and Safety at Work etc. Act 1974 (the Act) is the primary legislation covering health and safety in England, Scotland and Wales.

The Act mainly places legal duties on employers, the self-employed and, to a lesser extent, employees. The aim is to promote health and safety awareness and effective standards of health and safety management by every employer.

This chapter outlines what the Act is about and what is required.

2.1 Introduction

The Health and Safety at Work etc. Act 1974 (HSWA) is the primary piece of legislation covering occupational health and safety in Great Britain. The Health and Safety Executive (HSE) and Local Authorities are responsible for enforcing the Act.

The Act sets out the general duties that employers have towards their employees, the duties of employees, and the self-employed to persons other than their employees, as well as duties that employees have to themselves and each other.

These duties are qualified in the Act by the principle of 'so far as is reasonably practicable'. In other words, an employer does not have to take additional measures to avoid or reduce the risk if they are technically impossible or if the time, trouble or cost of the measures would be grossly disproportionate to the risk.

What the law requires is what good management and common sense would lead employers to do anyway: that is, to look at what the risks are and take sensible measures to tackle them.

It shall be the duty of every employer to ensure, so far as is reasonably practicable, the health, safety and welfare at work of all their employees.

For an explanation of *absolute, practicable* and *reasonably practicable* refer to Chapter A01 Health and safety law.

2.2 Aims and scope of the Act

The Health and Safety at Work etc. Act 1974 provides for a comprehensive, legislative framework to promote, stimulate and encourage high standards of a healthy and safe workplace.

Its ultimate aim is to promote health and safety awareness and effective standards of health and safety management by every employer.

One of the main aims of the Act is to **involve everyone** in matters of health and safety.

- Management.
- Employees.
- Self-employed.
- Employees' representatives.
- Controllers of premises.
- Manufacturers of plant, equipment and materials.

The Act also requires that adequate measures are taken to protect others (such as members of the public) where otherwise their health or safety would be at risk.

All persons at work are covered by the Act, with the exception of domestic servants in private households and some Crown employees.

The Act is an **enabling Act** that allows the Secretary of State to make further laws (regulations) without the need to pass another Act of Parliament. Regulations are laws, approved by Parliament. These are usually made under the Act following proposals from the Health and Safety Executive (HSE).

2.3 Relevant statutory provisions

The Act requires compliance with the relevant statutory provisions.

- The Act itself.
- Other health and safety legislation, as listed in Schedule 1 of the Act.
- All the legislation made under Section 15 of the Act. (This covers all health and safety regulations made since 1974.)

2.4 Main parts of the Act

The Act consists of four parts, shown below.

Part 1	Health, safety and welfare in the workplace.
Part 2	Employment Medical Advisory Service – functions and responsibilities.
Part 3	Building Regulations and relating amendments to the law.
Part 4	Miscellaneous and general provisions.

Managers, supervisors, safety supervisors, safety representatives and others with a responsibility for ensuring legal compliance will be mainly concerned with Part 1 of the Act.

2.4.1 Part 1. Health, safety and welfare in the workplace

The main provisions of Part 1 of the Act are shown below.

- ☑ Securing the health, safety and welfare of persons at work.
- ☑ Protecting persons, other than persons at work, against risks to health and safety, arising out of, or in connection with, the activities of persons at work.
- ☑ Duties of employees.
- ☑ Establishing the Health and Safety Commission and the HSE, which are to be generally responsible for enforcing and administering the Act, or any of the regulations made under it.
- ☑ The power of the Secretary of State to make regulations, the provision of regulations and repeal and modification of existing statutory provisions.
- ☑ Approval by the Health and Safety Commission of Approved Codes of Practice.
- ☑ Using Approved Codes of Practice in criminal proceedings.
- ☑ The powers of the HSE to make adequate arrangements for the enforcement of relevant statutory provisions, both in relation to this and other health and safety legislation, whether by appointing its own inspectors or transferring its powers to other Local Authorities.
- ☑ The appointment of inspectors in writing, specifying their powers and means for the enforcement of the Act.
- ☑ Improvement notices.
- ☑ Prohibition notices.
- ☑ Appeals procedures against improvement or prohibition notices.
- ☑ The provision for criminal offences and punishments.

2.4.2 Part 2. Employment Medical Advisory Service

The main provision of Part 2 of the Act is the continuation of the Employment Medical Advisory Service (EMAS). The responsibility for maintaining this service has been delegated by the Secretary of State to the HSE.

2.4.3 Part 3. Building Regulations

The main provision of Part 3 of the Act is the extension of the scope and coverage of the Building Regulations.

2.4.4 Part 4. General provisions

The main provision of Part 4 of the Act concerns amendments, repeals and modifications to other Acts or instruments.

These amendments affect (among other matters) general fire precautions, including means of escape in most factories, offices and shops. These can now be dealt with by the fire authorities. The HSE remains responsible for control over 'process risks', that is, risk of outbreak of fire associated with particular processes or particular substances.

In future, regulations may be made so that company reports will have to include information on health, safety and welfare arrangements.

2.5 Duty holders under the Act

The Act **mainly** places legal duties on employers, the self-employed and employees, but there are some exceptions.

- ☑ Section 4 places duties on the persons who control premises with regard to the health and safety of other persons who are not their employees.
- ☑ Section 6 places duties on the manufacturers, designers, importers and suppliers of equipment.
- ☑ Section 8 places a duty on all people to not intentionally or recklessly interfere with or misuse anything provided in the interests of health, safety or welfare.

A 02

2.5.1 Duties of employers

Part 1 of the Act places a general duty on every employer to ensure, so far as is **reasonably practicable**, the health, safety and welfare at work of all their employees.

The Act goes on to state that, so far as is reasonably practicable, the employer must meet the following requirements.

- ☑ Protect the health, safety and welfare at work of all their employees – Section 2(1).
- ☑ Provide and maintain plant and systems of work that are safe and without risk to health – Section 2(2)(a).
- ☑ Ensure safety and absence of risks in the use, handling, storage and transport of articles and substances – Section 2(2)(b).
- ☑ Provide adequate information, instruction, training and supervision, as is necessary, to ensure the health and safety of their employees – Section 2(2)(c).
- ☑ Provide and maintain a working environment that is safe, without risks to health and with safe access and egress – Section 2(2)(d).
- ☑ Provide and maintain a working environment that is safe, without risks to health and with adequate welfare and facilities arrangements – Section 2(2)(e).

Certain additional duties have been placed on the employer.

- ☑ Where five or more persons are employed, to prepare, publicise and revise as often as may be appropriate, a written statement of the employer's health and safety policy and the organisation and arrangements in force for implementing the policy – Section 2(3).
- ☑ To ensure, as far as is reasonably practicable, that the conduct of their work does not endanger persons not in their employment who may be affected by operations under their control, for example, sub-contractors or the public - Section 3(1).

The HSE recommends that, as good practice, companies give information about health and safety performance in their shareholders' or annual report.

In certain circumstances employers must provide information to others about those aspects of their undertaking that might affect health and safety. This duty is explicit in the Construction (Design and Management) Regulations.

Trade unions recognised by the management at the workplace have the right to appoint safety representatives from within the workforce.

Section 2(4), (6) and (7) state that employers must achieve the following.

- ☑ Provide for the appointment, by recognised trade unions, of safety representatives from the employees, in order to consult with, as appropriate.
- ☑ Establish safety committees when requested by at least two safety representatives.

Employers must **not** levy a charge, or permit any employee to be charged, for anything required to be provided in pursuance of any of the relevant statutory provisions - Section 9.

For further details of the employers duty to consult refer to Chapter A01 Health and safety law.

2.5.2 Duties of employees

The Act places two general duties on employees.

- ☑ To exercise reasonable care for the health and safety of themselves or others who may be affected by their acts or omissions at work – Section 7(a).
- ☑ To co-operate with the employer, as far as is necessary, to enable them (the employer) to comply with their legal duties in health and safety matters – Section 7(b).

Employees also have duties under various other regulations that expand on these general duties (for example, Section 14 of the Management of Health and Safety at Work Regulations).

2.5.3 Duties of the self-employed

A general duty is placed on the self-employed to conduct their undertaking in such a way as to ensure, so far as is **reasonably practicable**, that they and other persons are not exposed to risks to health and safety. In many ways, the self-employed person has similar duties to an employer, including giving information to persons other than their employees about those aspects of their undertaking that might affect their health and safety - Section 3(2) and (3).

Self-employed builders fined for illegal asbestos removal

Two self-employed builders were sentenced for exposing householders, as well as themselves, to asbestos. The builders were prosecuted after they illegally removed and broke up asbestos panels from a home.

Samples were taken to test for asbestos and the results revealed that asbestos was present. However, the HSE's investigation concluded that by the time the test results were known, the builders had already broken up the asbestos insulating boards (AIBs) with a hammer and removed them.

Neither of the builders held the necessary licence to remove the asbestos boards. Nor did they carry out, or ask to see, an asbestos survey, which is required by law before any demolition or refurbishment work is undertaken.

In failing to take adequate steps to prevent both the exposure to and spread of asbestos fibres generated by their work, they put the householders, themselves and others at risk of inhaling the potentially harmful airborne fibres. The subsequent clean-up of the site cost more than £6,500.

Both builders pleaded guilty to a breach of the Health and Safety at Work Act 1974. They were individually fined a total of £2,000 and ordered to pay costs of £1,200.

Speaking after the prosecution, an HSE inspector said: 'An estimated 70% of properties contain asbestos. It is illegal to undertake any work which will disturb the fabric of the building without carrying out and obtaining the results of an asbestos survey.

The type of work being undertaken should have been carried out by a builder who holds the necessary licence, in a safe manner and with the necessary control measures. Instead (the builders) exposed the householders and others – including themselves – to potentially harmful airborne asbestos fibres. They also demonstrated a complete disregard for the law'.

Section 3(2) of the Health and Safety at Work Act 1974 states: it shall be the duty of every self-employed person to conduct their undertaking in such a way as to ensure, so far as is reasonably practicable, that they and other persons (not being their employees) who may be affected thereby are not exposed to risks to their health or safety.

2.5.4 Duties of all people

This section of the Act places a duty on all persons to not intentionally or recklessly interfere with or misuse anything provided in the interests of health, safety and welfare – Section 8.

This can apply to both employees and non-employees.

2.5.5 Duties of manufacturers, designers, importers and suppliers

A general duty is placed on any person who manufactures, designs, imports or supplies any article, material or substance for use at work to ensure, so far as is reasonably practicable, that articles and substances are, by design and construction, safe and without risks to health when being used, set, cleaned or maintained by persons at work.

e.g.

Information on design noise levels under normal working conditions should be supplied if noise levels may be a risk to health, or exceed the lower exposure action value specified in the Control of Noise at Work Regulations. Similarly, manufacturers of tools that may be a source of hand-arm vibration must provide details of the levels of vibration generated.

More specifically, a duty exists to ensure that arrangements are made to carry out the necessary testing, examination and research of any article, material or substance, and that steps are taken to provide adequate information about any conditions necessary to ensure that it will be safe when used.

A general duty is placed on installers or erectors of any article for use at work to ensure, so far as is reasonably practicable, that it is safe and without risk to health when used by persons at work - Section 6(3).

2.5.6 Duties of those in control of premises

Duties are imposed on anyone who is in control of non-domestic premises to ensure the health and safety of anyone, who is not an employee, who enters those premises to carry out work.

The duties also apply to premises where machinery, equipment or substances are provided for the use of others.

The person in control of non-domestic premises is generally the owner, occupier or other person who has specific obligations for maintenance or repair of those premises by virtue of a contract or tenancy agreement.

A 02

2.6 Health and Safety Executive

The HSE has been given certain powers and duties under the Act. The powers may also be exercised by Local Authority environmental health officers on certain smaller sites and in offices.

The enforcement of all health and safety law is carried out under the provisions of the Health and Safety at Work Act 1974. This means that methods of enforcement are the same throughout the country.

The Health and Safety Executive (HSE) is responsible for maintaining a force of health and safety inspectors, some of whom specialise in construction industry activities.

Prosecution and enforcement notices have increased over the last six years and the average fine per offence has also increased. In 2011-12 there were eight cases where the fines were £20,000 or above, two of which involved fines of £500,000 each.

Health and safety inspectors have wide ranging powers, vested in them by the HSWA. They also have enforcement powers under the Regulatory Reform (Fire Safety) Order (RR(FS)O). Below is a summary of the main powers that inspectors and Local Authority environmental health officers possess. Officers of the local fire and rescue service also have enforcement powers when dealing with matters under the RR(FS)O.

- Prosecute a company or individual for a breach of health and safety law.
- Visit or carry out an inspection of a workplace, at a reasonable time, without giving prior notice.
- Issue a prohibition or improvement notice.
- Stop the further use of equipment that is considered to be a serious risk to health or safety.
- Investigate accidents or dangerous occurrences.
- Require that any designated part of a premises remains undisturbed for as long as is deemed necessary.
- Investigate a particular work activity or any plant or equipment following a complaint or accident.
- Take measurements or photographs as necessary.
- Inspect or take copies of any books or records.
- Demand the full co-operation of any persons to assist them in their duties.
- Demand information from employers or employees and require them to sign a statement of their answers.
- Remove or make safe any article or substance considered to be a source of danger or serious personal injury.
- Require additional fire precautions work to be carried out on a construction site.
- Provide information for employers and employees about hazards that may affect their health and safety at work.
- Act as a source of information on health, safety and welfare at work.

www.

The HSE offers a range of services to assist employers and employees. Many publications are produced each year – with some at no charge or downloadable from its website.

2.6.1 Investigation

Inspectors are given a general right to examine and investigate as necessary – Section 20. They may:

- enter premises (accompanied by a police officer or other authorised person if necessary), taking with them any equipment or material required by them for the purposes of the examination
- direct that anything shall be left undisturbed if required for examination or investigation
- take measurements, samples, photographs and such recordings as may be necessary
- have dismantled or tested any article or substance considered dangerous, or take possession of any article for examination and evidence.

Inspectors may inspect or take copies of books or documents. They may demand from an employee any information they think necessary and can ask the employee to sign a declaration of the truth of their answers. In general, they can demand the full co-operation of any person to provide them with such facilities and assistance as they may deem necessary.

2.6.2 Advisory

Inspectors also act as a source of information and advice. It is their duty to tell employee representatives (safety representatives or trade union-appointed safety representatives) or the employees about anything that may affect their health and safety at work. This information should be similar to that given to the employer.

2.6.3 Enforcement options

Inspectors can use any of the powers listed in the following table against any person taking part in, or in control of, any work activity or piece of equipment. *Any person* means an employer, self-employed person, a supplier, or the employee.

1. Informal	Inspectors may give advice on compliance in the case of minor breaches.
2. Formal letter	A formal letter may contain details of breaches and the action needed to comply with the legislation. It may also contain more detailed and formalised advice. Whilst visiting a site, an inspector can prepare an instant visit report with a date agreed for work to be completed.
3. Improvement notice	Where a breach is more serious, the inspector may issue an improvement notice, which will outline the work required and the date for completion. This will be at least 21 days from the date of receipt. *(Refer to Appendix A for an example of an improvement notice.)*
4. Prohibition notice	If an activity involves, or is likely to involve, a serious risk of personal injury, the inspector may serve a prohibition notice to stop that activity either immediately or at the end of the period specified. *(Refer to Appendix B for an example of a prohibition notice.)*
5. Prosecution	In addition to the enforcement outlined above, the inspector may consider that it is also necessary to prosecute. This can be either in a Magistrate's Court or Crown Court.

Failure to comply with an improvement notice

A building company was found guilty of breaching the Health and Safety at Work Act, by failing to comply with an improvement notice, and also found guilty of breaching the Construction (Design and Management) Regulations.

During three months the company had been served with three prohibition notices and two improvement notices. The site manager was also issued with a prohibition notice because the operation of the site was far below minimum legal safety standards.

The company was fined a total of £40,000 and ordered to pay costs of £10,035.

After the hearing the HSE inspector said: 'If the HSE visits a construction site and has to issue prohibition notices preventing further work, that in itself shows that there is a very real and immediate risk to workers there, and possibly to members of the public.

(The company) failed on several fronts to safeguard the workforce from risks that are well known in the construction industry. They either did not identify those risks or neglected to manage them effectively.

Proper management of work activities and competent site supervision are essential, but the company fell well below the required standards'.

Section 33(1)(g) of the Health and Safety at Work Act states: it is an offence for a person to contravene any requirement or prohibition imposed by an improvement notice or a prohibition notice (including any such notice as modified on appeal).

Contravention of certain requirements of the Act can lead to summary prosecution in a Magistrate's Court (or Sheriff's Court in Scotland). In October 1992, under the provisions of the Criminal Justice Act, the current maximum fine that may be imposed by a Magistrate's Court or Sheriff's Court was raised from £2,000 to £5,000. This was subsequently raised to £20,000 by the Health and Safety (Offences) Act.

Contravention of other provisions can result in either summary prosecution, or an indictment in the Crown Court (High Court in Scotland). The maximum penalty, on summary conviction, in a Magistrate's Court is £20,000 per offence, or six months' imprisonment, or both. For certain serious offences, which are dealt with at a Crown Court, there is no limit to the fine, and prison sentences of up to two years can be imposed.

Breach of the Health and Safety at Work Act

A company director pleaded guilty to breaching Section 37 of the Health and Safety at Work Act, after consenting to a worker working at height in an excavator bucket. He was sentenced to eight months in prison (suspended for two years), disqualified from acting as company director for three years, and fined £32,000 with £11,000 costs.

**Magistrate's Court: up to £20,000 fine and up to six months' imprisonment.
Crown Court: unlimited fine and up to two years' imprisonment.**

A
02

2.6.4 Appeals

Anyone served with an improvement or prohibition notice has the right to appeal to an industrial tribunal. This must be done within 21 days of the issue of the notice. The tribunal may cancel, confirm or modify the notice on appeal, following the issue of either of the following notices.

- ☑ An improvement notice: the notice will be suspended until the tribunal meets and decides the issue.
- ☑ A prohibition notice: the notice will stand until the appeal has been decided, or the tribunal orders it to be suspended.

Offences under the Act can be committed by individuals as well as by corporate bodies, such as limited companies. When an offence has been committed with the help or knowledge of a director, manager, company secretary or other company official, that individual person may be prosecuted as well as the company.

The same duty is placed on the Crown (for example, Government departments and the armed forces) except that the employer cannot be prosecuted. However, individual members of that organisation can be prosecuted for offences they commit, but not for those committed by their employer - Section 37.

Where a person has been prosecuted for failing to comply with a duty or requirement of the Act, and is claiming that it was not reasonably practicable for them to carry out that duty or requirement, it is the responsibility of that person to prove that it was not reasonably practicable to comply, and that there was no reasonably practicable alternative way in which they could have carried out that duty or requirement - Section 40.

2.7 Fees for intervention

The HSE introduced a fee for intervention (FFI) cost recovery scheme with effect from 1 October 2012, under the Health and Safety (Fees) Regulations.

The regulations apply to businesses and individuals who are regulated by the HSE.

These regulations place a duty on the HSE to recover its costs for carrying out its regulatory functions from those found to be in material breach of health and safety law (such as investigations, inspections and enforcement action).

A material breach is when, in the opinion of the HSE inspector, there has been a contravention of health and safety law that is serious enough to require them to notify the person in material breach of that opinion in writing (for example, a notice, prosecution or letter).

For examples of notices that can be issued under the Health and Safety (Fees) Regulations refer to appendices C, D and E.

The HSE will charge an hourly rate for all the time spent by the inspector in identifying the breach, including visits, letter writing, drafting notices, and so on, and subsequently ensuring corrective actions have been taken.

The table below shows the number of invoices raised and the revenue generated from October 2012 to March 2013 for all sectors.

	Oct-Nov 2012	Dec 2012-Jan 2013	Feb-March 2013	Total for 2012-13
Number of invoices	1,418	1,807	2,541	5,766
Revenue invoiced	£727,645	£857,254	£1,088,874	£2,673,773
Average invoice	£513	£474	£428	£464

The table shows that the number of invoices and the revenue being generated is increasing. Fees incurred for investigations may be significantly higher than the current average.

The table below gives an invoice breakdown by sector.

	Oct-Nov 2012	Dec 2012-Jan 2013	Feb-March 2013
Agriculture	£15,800	£17,500	£22,300
Extractive utilities	£29,000	£20,500	£53,900
Waste/water management	£19,000	£29,000	£44,500
Services	£148,000	£207,000	£214,500
Construction	£224,400	£206,300	£291,500
Manufacturing	£291,300	£375,200	£451,900

(Figures in table have been rounded.)

The HSE will proactively inspect those businesses that are known to be high risk – construction businesses are one of these. The HSE will also visit businesses and individuals if they have information that people may be at unnecessary risk, irrespective of the business sector, or if there has been a reported incident.

Businesses and organisations are advised that if the HSE identifies a material breach of health and safety law corrective action should be taken promptly, so minimal time is spent by the investigating inspector and hence the fee will be less than if corrective action is delayed.

The HSE and Government believe it is right that businesses and organisations that break health and safety laws should pay for the HSE's time in putting matters right, investigating and taking enforcement action. Without FFI this is paid for from the public purse.

In 2014 an independent report concluded that during the first 18 months of implementation the FFI scheme was working effectively and should be retained. The following conclusions were also made.

- Fears that FFI would be used to generate revenue have proven to be unfounded.
- While not popular with some inspectors and duty holders, it has been embedded effectively and applied consistently.
- There is no viable alternative that can achieve the same aims.

www.

The following information can be found on the HSE website.

- **Guidance on the application of fee for intervention (FFI).**
- **Fee for intervention: What you need to know.**
- **A full FFI report.**
- **Enforcement management model.**

2.8 Health and Safety Commission

The Health and Safety Commission (HSC) was established under the provisions of The Health and Safety at Work Act 1974 and, until its merger with the HSE on 1 April 2008, had an overall role in advising the Government on all health and safety matters.

The merger of the HSC and the HSE to form a single regulatory body took place after extensive consultation, with the aim of strengthening the links between the strategy and delivery. The single regulatory body is called the Health and Safety Executive which, in addition to incorporating the former Health and Safety Commission as the Board, retains all of its original function and powers.

The Health and Safety Executive (HSE) is now the single regulatory statutory body, working in accordance with directions and guidance from the Board. It enforces legal requirements, as well as providing an advisory service.

The board of the HSE comprises representatives of both sides of industry and Local Authorities. It has responsibility for developing policies in the health and safety field. The chairperson of the board is appointed by the Government.

2.9 Employment Medical Advisory Service

The Employment Medical Advisory Service (EMAS) acts as the medical arm of the HSE. It is the main channel of medical advice to the inspectorates within the executive, as well as giving advice to employers. EMAS also publishes leaflets under four subject headings.

- General information.
- Specific health hazards.
- Research and guidance notes.
- Medical series.

These are normally available from EMAS headquarters. The address of the office of the EMAS should be detailed on the approved health and safety law poster.

2.10 Health and Safety (Enforcing Authority) Regulations

The responsibility for enforcing health and safety is broadly split between the HSE and the Local Authority. These regulations provide for the transfer of the responsibility for the enforcement of health and safety legislation between the HSE and the Local Authority (and vice versa) in certain circumstances. Within the Local Authority, environmental health officers are usually the enforcing officers.

2.10.1 Local Authority enforcement

Schedule 1 of the regulations lists the premises for which the Local Authority will be responsible. These include offices, shops, catering establishments, hotels, residential homes, places of sport, most places of entertainment and places of religion.

2.10.2 HSE enforcement

If a category of workplace is not specified in Schedule 1, the HSE will be the enforcing authority. Some examples of workplaces for which the HSE is the enforcing authority are shown below.

- Building and construction sites.
- Mines and quarries.
- Manufacturing industry.
- Fairgrounds.
- Hospitals.
- Educational establishments.
- Agriculture.

2.10.2.1 Transfer of responsibility for enforcement

Where construction work is carried out on premises for which the Local Authority is normally the enforcing authority, and the work is to be carried out by persons who do not normally work at those premises, the HSE will become the enforcing authority for the duration of the work in the following circumstances.

- When the work is notifiable to the HSE by virtue of the Construction (Design and Management) Regulations.
- If, in whole or part, it involves work to the external fabric or other external parts of the structure.
- Where work is carried out in a physically segregated area of the premises and work activities normally carried out in that area are suspended.
- When work involves the installation, maintenance or repair of gas or electrical systems.
- If it involves the use of ionising radiation (in some cases only).

2.11 Examples of health and safety court cases

The following are brief details of two court cases that arose out of failings in the management of health and safety.

e.g.

Regina -v- Swan Hunter Shipbuilders Ltd and Telemeter Installations Ltd

This important Court of Appeal case, resulting from a prosecution under Sections 2 and 3 of the Health and Safety at Work Act 1974, demonstrated that an employer (the main contractor) has a duty to inform, instruct and supervise not only its own employees but also other workers (sub-contractors) who might, by their behaviour, endanger the main contractor's employees.

e.g.

Regina -v- Associated Octel Company Ltd

This equally important Court of Appeal case demonstrates that under Section 3 of the Health and Safety at Work Act 1974 an employer can be prosecuted for failing to secure the safety of an independent contractor's employees, whether or not it has been involved with that third party's work. If an employer asks an independent contractor to do work that forms part of the overall job being carried out by the employer, the employer must stipulate the conditions needed to avoid risks to health and safety and that are reasonably practicable to protect that contractor's workforce.

The HSE website breaks down regulations into easy to follow topic areas, industry sectors (such as construction) and different levels of guidance aimed at company owners down to employees. It also contains ACoPs and guidance, which are available as free downloads.

www.

Copies of all acts and regulations can be downloaded from the Government's legislation website.

Appendix A – Example of an improvement notice

Health and Safety at Work Act 1974

HSE
Health & Safety
Executive

The Health and Safety at Work Act 1974, Sections 21, 23 and

Serial Number
I

Improvement notice

	Name
	Address
	Trading as*
Inspector' s full name	I,
Inspector's official designation	one of Her Majesty's Inspectors of Being an Inspector appointed by an instrument in writing made pursuant to section 19 of the said Act and entitled to issue the notice
Official address	of Telephone number
	hereby give you notice that I am of the opinion that
Location of premises or place of activity	at
	you, as an employer / self employed person / person wholly or partly in control of the premises / other* are contravening*/ have contravened in circumstances that make it likely that the contravention will continue or be repeated* the following statutory provisions:
	The reasons for my said opinion are:
	and I hereby require you to remedy the said contraventions or, as the case may be, the matters occasioning them by (and I direct that the measures specified in the Schedule which forms part of this notice shall be taken to remedy the said contraventions or matters)*
	Signature Date
	*An Improvement Notice is also being served on of related to the matters contained in this notice
Environment and Safety Information Act 1988	This is a relevant notice for the purposes of the Environment and Safety Information Act 1988 YES/NO* This page only will form the register entry.*
	Signature Date

LP1 (rev 04.97) *SEE NOTES OVERLEAF* ** delete as appropriate*

Appendix B – Example of a prohibition notice

Health and Safety at Work Act 1974

The Health and Safety at Work Act 1974, Sections 22, 23 and 24

Serial Number
P

HSE
Health & Safety
Executive

Prohibition notice

	Name
	Address
	Trading as*
Inspector' s full name	I,
Inspector's official designation	one of Her Majesty's Inspectors of Being an Inspector appointed by an instrument in writing made pursuant to section 19 of the said Act and entitled to issue the notice
Official address	of Telephone number
	hereby give you notice that I am of the opinion that the following activities namely:
Location of premises or place of activity	which are being carried on by you / likely to be carried on by you / under your control* at
	involve, or will involve, a risk of serious personal injury, and that the matters which give rise / will give rise* to the said risks are:
	and that the said matters involve / will involve* contravention of the following statutory provisions:
	because
	and I hereby direct that the said activities shall not be carried on by you or under your control immediately / after* unless the said contraventions and matters have been remedied. I further direct that the measures specified in the schedule which forms part of this notice shall be taken to remedy the said contraventions or matters*
	Signature Date
	*A Prohibition Notice is also being served on
	of
	related to the matters contained in this notice
Environment and Safety Information Act 1988	This is a relevant notice for the purposes of the Environment and Safety Information Act 1988 YES/NO* This page only will form the register entry.*
	Signature Date

LP2 (rev 04.97) *SEE NOTES OVERLEAF* ** delete as appropriate*

Appendix C – Health and Safety (Fees) Regulations – Fee for intervention

HSE

Health and Safety
Executive

Notification of Contravention Enforcement Notices

Prohibition/Improvement* Notice No(s)...

.... [1]*[see overleaf]*

* *[amend as applicable]*

Health and Safety (Fees) Regulations 2012 ('the Fees Regulations 2012') - Fee for Intervention

Under regulations 23 and 24 of the Fees Regulations 2012, HSE will recover its costs for the work it does in relation to dealing with certain contraventions of health and safety law. These contraventions are known as 'material breaches'.[2] *[see overleaf]* This cost recovery is called 'Fee for Intervention' or 'FFI'.

This Notification of Contravention and the accompanying Prohibition/ Improvement* Notice(s) (referenced above) confirm that the contraventions on the Prohibition/Improvement* Notice constitute a material breach. HSE will recover from you the costs that it incurs in consequence of any contravention that is a material breach. The costs for the whole visit where a material breach is first identified are recoverable, along with other associated work.[3] *[see overleaf]*

* *[amend as applicable]*

HSE will send you an invoice for the costs incurred.[4] *[see overleaf]*

Please see overleaf[5] for advice on how to find more information on health and safety. *[see overleaf]*

Inspector signature: **Date:**

Recipient name and position:

Recipient signature: **Date:**

NoC EN *(10.12)*

Information

1. You should read the Prohibition or Improvement Notice and the accompanying notes on the rear of the Notice carefully. Compliance will be measured against the content of the Notice.

2. A material breach is when, in the opinion of the HSE Inspector, there is or has been a contravention of health and safety law that requires them to issue notice in writing of that opinion to the dutyholder. This Notification of Contravention and the accompanying Prohibition or Improvement Notice is written notice of my opinion.

3. There are exemptions and disapplications, where HSE cannot recover its costs for carrying out its functions. These exemptions and disapplications are detailed in HSE47 - *Guidance on the application of Fee for Intervention* at http://www.hse.gov.uk/pubns/hse47.pdf.

4. Under regulation 25(5) of the Fees Regulations 2012, you have the right to dispute the invoice. You can find further information about Fee for Intervention and details of the terms on which you can dispute an invoice in the leaflet HSE48 - *Fee for Intervention: What you need to know.* More detailed information is given in HSE47 - *Guidance on the application of Fee for Intervention* at http://www.hse.gov.uk/pubns/hse47.pdf.

5. For further information about health and safety, visit HSE's website at www.hse.gov.uk. You can view and download HSE guidance online and order priced publications from the website. HSE priced publications are also available from bookshops.

Appendix D – Health and Safety at Work Act – Visit by HM Inspector of health and safety

HSE

Health and Safety Executive

Notification of Contravention

Sheet of

To:

HM Inspector:

Address:

Office address and telephone number:

Head Office:

Manager:

HEALTH AND SAFETY AT WORK ETC ACT 1974
VISIT BY HM INSPECTOR OF HEALTH AND SAFETY

I carried out a visit on .... and discussed health and safety matters with

....

The contraventions of health and safety law listed on this notification were found during my visit.[1] A Prohibition Notice/Improvement* Notice was also served at my visit.*[2] *[amend as applicable] [see overleaf]*

You should take action to comply with the law on the matters listed by .... (unless stated otherwise on this notification). Please let me know when you have taken the necessary action.* A return visit may be made to ensure the appropriate action has been taken.* *[amend as applicable]*

I have given a copy of this notification to .... as a representative of your employees.* I have left a copy of this notification for the information of your employees. The contents of it should be brought to the attention of your employees.* *[amend as applicable]*

Health and Safety (Fees) Regulations 2012 ('the Fees Regulations 2012') - Fee for Intervention

Under regulations 23 and 24 of the Fees Regulations 2012, HSE will recover its costs for the work it does in relation to dealing with certain contraventions of health and safety law. These contraventions are known as 'material breaches'.[3] *[see overleaf]* This cost recovery is called 'Fee for Intervention' or 'FFI'.

You are notified in the final column of the **attached** sheet(s) if a contravention is a material breach. HSE will recover from you the costs that it incurs in consequence of any contravention that is a material breach. The costs for the whole visit where a material breach is first identified are recoverable, along with other associated work.[4] *[see overleaf]*

HSE will send you an invoice for the costs incurred.[5] *[see overleaf]*

Please see overleaf[6] for advice on how to find more information on health and safety.

Inspector signature: **Date:**

Recipient name and position:

Recipient signature: **Date:**

NoC1 *(10.12)* **Company ID:** **Site ID:**

Information

1. Where an inspection was carried out it sampled how you are complying with your legal responsibilities and did not examine all aspects of your business. It is your responsibility to ensure the health and safety of employees and others, such as members of the public, who may be affected by the way you run your business.

2. If you have been served with a Prohibition or Improvement Notice, you should:

- read the Prohibition or Improvement Notice carefully as compliance will be measured against its content;
- read the Notes on the rear of the Prohibition or Improvement Notice; and
- please note that any advice on compliance with the Notice contained in the accompanying table of contraventions does not form part of the Notice.

3. A material breach is when, in the opinion of the HSE Inspector, there is or has been a contravention of health and safety law that requires them to issue notice in writing of that opinion to the dutyholder. This Notification of Contravention is written notice of my opinion.

4. There are exemptions and disapplications where HSE cannot recover its costs for carrying out its functions. These exemptions and disapplications are detailed in HSE47 - *Guidance on the application of Fee for Intervention* at http://www.hse.gov.uk/pubns/hse47.pdf.

5. Under regulation 25(5) of the Fees Regulations 2012 you have the right to dispute the invoice. You can find further information about Fee for Intervention and details of the terms on which you can dispute an invoice in the leaflet HSE48 - *Fee for Intervention: What you need to know.* More detailed information is given in HSE47 - *Guidance on the application of Fee for Intervention* at http://www.hse.gov.uk/pubns/hse47.pdf.

6. For further information about health and safety, visit HSE's website at www.hse.gov.uk. You can view and download HSE guidance online and order priced publications from the website. HSE priced publications are also available from bookshops.

Appendix E – Health and Safety at Work Act – Contraventions of health and safety law

HSE

Health and Safety Executive

Notification of Contravention

Sheet of

HEALTH AND SAFETY AT WORK ETC ACT 1974
CONTRAVENTIONS OF HEALTH AND SAFETY LAW

Nº	**Relevant law contravened** (inc section or regulation) *[see overleaf]*	**Reasons for Inspector's opinion and action required to achieve compliance with the law** *[what is wrong, why it is wrong and what is required to comply with the law]*	**Material breach*** *[Yes / No]*

Inspector signature: **Date of visit:**

Recipient signature and position: **Date:**

* For which a fee is payable to HSE under the Fee for Intervention scheme.

NoC1a *(10.12)* **Company ID:** **Site ID:**

Legal Reference List

Health and safety law enforced by HSE for which costs can be recovered under Fee For Intervention.
[NB: Refer to most recently updated versions of each piece of legislation to ensure that you take account of all amendments.]

A - Confined Spaces Regulations 1997
B - Construction (Design and Management) Regulations 2007
C - Control of Asbestos Regulations 2012
D - Control of Noise at Work Regulations 2005
E - Control of Substances Hazardous to Health Regulations 2002
F - Control of Vibration at Work Regulations 2005
G - Dangerous Substances and Explosive Atmospheres Regulations 2002
H - Electricity at Work Regulations 1989
I - Gas Safety (Installation and Use) Regulations 1998
J - Health and Safety at Work etc Act 1974
K - Health and Safety (First Aid) Regulations 1981
L - Ionising Radiations Regulations 1999
M - Lifting Operations and Lifting Equipment Regulations 1998
N - Management of Health and Safety at Work Regulations 1999
O - Manual Handling Operations Regulations 1992
P - Personal Protective Equipment at Work Regulations 1992
Q - Pressure Systems Safety Regulations 2000
R - Provision and Use of Work Equipment Regulations 1998
S - Quarries Regulations 1999
T - Safety Representatives and Safety Committees Regulations 1977
U - Work at Height Regulations 2005
V - Workplace (Health, Safety and Welfare) Regulations 1992

Health and safety law enforced by HSE for which costs cannot be recovered under Fee For Intervention

W - Control of Pesticides Regulations 1986
X - Employers' Liability (Compulsory Insurance) Act 1969
Y - Health and Safety (Consultation with Employees) Regulations 1996

Appendix F – Prosecution under the HSWA, the Company Directors Disqualification Act and the Fraud Act

Two directors prosecuted following fatal incident

A businessman, who was disqualified from being a company director, was jailed for serious fraud and safety offences. A second businessman was given a suspended prison sentence for similar offences.

The two were sentenced following joint proceedings brought by the Department for Business Innovation and Skills (BIS) and the Health and Safety Executive (HSE). The safety offence related to the tragic death of a 40 year-old worker.

The first director was jailed for a total of 26 months; 16 months for a breach of Section 2(1) of the Health and Safety at Work etc. Act 1974; 10 months for a breach of Section 2 of the Fraud Act 2006; and a total of eight months concurrent for four breaches of Section 13 of the Company Directors Disqualification Act 1986. He was also disqualified from being a company director for a maximum of 15 years.

The second director was given a 12 month prison sentence, suspended for two years, after admitting the same breach of the Health and Safety at Work etc. Act, and a concurrent six months, also suspended, after pleading guilty to aiding and abetting the first director in his disqualification. He was disqualified as a director for seven years, ordered to pay £8,000 toward prosecution costs and given 150 hours community service.

The safety offences related to the directors' running of their now insolvent company, and become apparent following a fatal incident where a worker was crushed by a two tonne metal sand moulding box. The box fell from the lifting chains of a crane the worker was using to manoeuvre it. Colleagues scrambled to free him, but he was pronounced dead at the scene by paramedics.

The HSE investigated the death and identified serious concerns with the systems of work in place at the time, and with the lifting equipment. They became aware of the Companies Act offences and a joint investigation with BIS was undertaken.

The HSE found that the crane at the centre of the incident had not been checked and tested as the law requires, and there were inadequate provisions in place covering competency, supervision and training. The court heard the incident could have been prevented, had the system of work been reviewed and properly assessed. HSE inspectors also identified problems with lead exposure at the company. The control and health surveillance measures were insufficient, meaning workers were being exposed to potentially harmful levels of lead without realising it.

The court was told that at the time of the worker's death the company was the subject of three improvement notices served by the HSE following earlier visits. A number of important safety improvements were required, but few had been satisfactorily implemented, largely, claimed the management team, because of financial constraints. The HSE argued the fatal incident could have been avoided had the necessary changes in the relevant enforcement notices taken place.

The company was also sentenced for a breach of Section 2(1) of the Health and Safety at Work etc. Act, after a guilty plea was submitted on behalf of the insolvent firm by its administrators. The court imposed a fine of £100,000.

The court was told how the first director had previously been disqualified from acting as a company director for 12 years. However, he had contravened two orders by acting in that capacity in no fewer than four separate companies over a five year period, including at The Company. He was also responsible for the cross-firing of cheques, which were written from the bank account of one of the companies, which was no longer trading, to provide funds to The Company. BIS investigators established that The Company drew almost £92,500 in this way, taking advantage of a short window after the cheques were presented but before they bounced.

The investigators also established that the second director aided and abetted the first director as the registered director of The Company, performing tasks, such as writing blank cheques for the first director to use, but not fulfilling the responsibilities of being the director of the company, allowing the first director to run the business.

In his sentencing comments the judge said that the defendant had behaved in a disgraceful way and had been culpable of extremely shoddy business practice.

After reading a statement from the worker's father, the judge said the impact of the incident had been devastating: 'It was harrowing, and underlines the personal tragedy that could have been avoided'.

After sentencing the HSE director of operations said: 'The safety standards at The Company fell well short of those required, as the directors were only too aware. They knew improvements were needed to protect workers like the deceased and they had clear responsibilities as senior management to ensure the necessary changes were implemented. Sadly one of the many areas that was seemingly overlooked was the system of work surrounding the overhead crane. Had this been properly assessed then the deceased's tragic death could have been prevented'.

The worker's father commented: 'I brought my son up since he was an infant and cared for him all his life until his death. His passing has left a huge empty void in my life, a devastating loss that I will never recover from'.

The deputy chief investigation officer from BIS said: 'Individuals are disqualified from being company directors for good reason, usually because of conduct which shows them to be unfit to operate a business. This case shows the tragic consequences of the defendant ignoring his disqualification'.

(Source HSE.)

03

Construction (Design and Management) Regulations

Contents

Supporting information

G: Checklists and forms

GT 700 Toolbox talks

Overview

The Construction (Design and Management) Regulations (CDM) are the main regulations that cover the management of health, safety and welfare on construction projects. The current regulations (in force from 6 April 2015) replace the CDM Regulations 2007 and apply to all construction projects, regardless of size, duration and the nature of work.

This chapter outlines what the regulations are about, what they require, what needs to be done and by whom.

3.1 Introduction

The CDM Regulations were first introduced in 1994 and subsequently revised in 2007. Following the requirements of Directive 92/57/EEC to implement the minimum safety and health requirements at temporary or mobile construction sites, and to support the strategic objectives of improved co-ordination, better value for money, improved efficiency and use of technology changes in *Construction 2025* (the Government's industrial strategy for construction), the regulations have been amended to reflect these required changes.

Below are the main changes within CDM 2015.

- ☑ The replacement of CDM co-ordinator with **principal designer**. This means that the responsibility for co-ordination of the pre-construction phase (which is crucial to the management of any successful construction project) will rest with the designer, who could be an organisation or an individual on a smaller project.
- ☑ Recognition of the influence and importance of the **client** as the head of the supply chain and as the party best placed to set standards throughout a project.
- ☑ By splitting **competence** into its component parts of skills, knowledge, training and experience and, if they are an organisation the organisational capability, provides clarity for the industry to assess and demonstrate that construction project teams have the right attributes to deliver a healthy and safe project.
- ☑ The technical standards set out in Part 4 remain essentially unchanged from CDM 2007 and the targeting and enforcement policy from the Health and Safety Executive (HSE), as a proportionate and modern regulator, also remains unchanged.
- ☑ The new CDM Regulations will apply to domestic client projects, although client duties will normally be transferred to the contractor or principal contractor or, if the client wishes to make a specific appointment, the designer.

The CDM Regulations are subject to **transitional provisions**. These apply to projects that started before CDM 2015 came into force and will continue beyond that date. The transitional provisions will run for six months (from 6 April 2015 to 6 October 2015). If the CDM co-ordinator has already been appointed, a principal designer must be appointed to replace the CDM co-ordinator within six months (by 6 October 2015), unless the project comes to an end before that date. For projects that involve more than one contractor and start on or after 6 April 2015 the client must appoint a principal designer, not a CDM co-ordinator. Further details of transitional arrangements are detailed in Regulation 37.

The appointed CDM co-ordinator should comply with the duties contained in paragraph 5 of Schedule 4 of CDM 2015. These duties reflect the existing duties of the CDM co-ordinator under CDM 2007 but also reflect the arrangements under CDM 2015 relating to the construction phase and the health and safety file.

The CDM Regulations are about focusing attention on effective planning and management of all construction work, from design concept onwards. The aim is for health and safety considerations to be treated as a normal part of a project's development, not an afterthought or bolt-on extra. The object of CDM is to reduce the risk of harm to those that have to build, use, maintain and demolish structures.

The main aims of the regulations are listed below.

- ☑ Encourage everyone to work together to make health and safety an integral part of the design, construction and management of projects.
- ☑ Improve planning and management from day one to identify hazards so that they can be eliminated or properly managed.
- ☑ Have the right people, for the right job, at the right time to manage the risks on site.
- ☑ Encourage co-operation and co-ordination throughout the project.

Whilst CDM covers most of the construction-specific risks, it is important to ensure compliance with other relevant regulations, such as the Work at Height Regulations and the Control of Substances Hazardous to Health Regulations.

3.2 Important points

- ☑ Construction companies will have to comply with the revised regulations from 6 April 2015.
- ☑ Employers will need to provide information, instruction, training and supervision, with workers having their needs assessed against the needs of the job and employers to meet the gap in skills and knowledge through appropriate training.
- ☑ CDM Regulations will apply to domestic client projects.
- ☑ All building and renovation work (for example, work shown in property development companies) will be covered by the CDM Regulations.

- ☑ Under CDM 2015 the trigger to notification carries no additional requirements.
- ☑ On a project where there is more than one contractor a principal contractor will need to be appointed.
- ☑ Designers and contractors should be appointed at the earliest opportunity to help them prepare for and plan the project.
- ☑ Everyone controlling site work has health and safety responsibilities.
- ☑ Checking that working conditions are healthy and safe before work begins, and ensuring that the proposed work is not going to put others at risk, requires planning and organisation.
- ☑ A project is notifiable if the construction work on a construction site is scheduled to:
  - – last longer than 30 working days and have more than 20 workers working simultaneously at any point in the project, or
  - – exceed 500 person days.
- ☑ CDM is supported by a regulatory package, which includes the CDM Regulations, HSE CDM legal (L) series guidance and industry guidance.
- ☑ A legal (L) series guidance supports the regulations and details the legal requirements for CDM. It should be used to help anyone who has duties to comply with the regulations.

www. **The legal (L) series guidance is available on the HSE website.**

A series of industry guidance for the five duty holders and one for **workers** set out in practical terms what actions are required by them to deliver a safe and healthy project. These have been written by the Construction Industry Advisory Committee (CONIAC) with small businesses in mind.

The **five duty holders** under the CDM Regulations are listed below.

- ☑ Clients (including domestic clients).
- ☑ Principal designers.
- ☑ Designers.
- ☑ Principal contractors.
- ☑ Contractors.

www. **Industry guidance notes for each duty holder are available on the CITB website.**

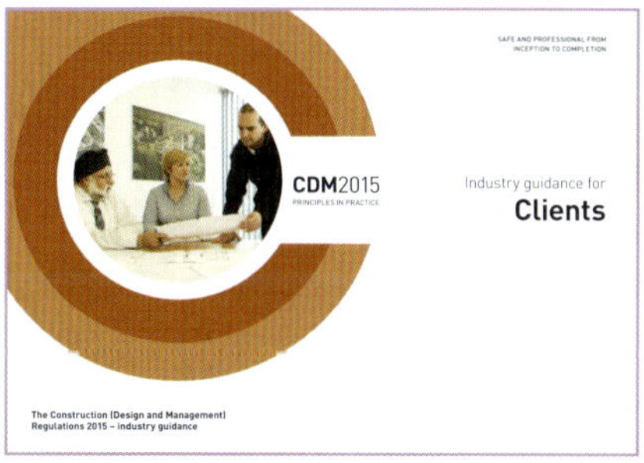

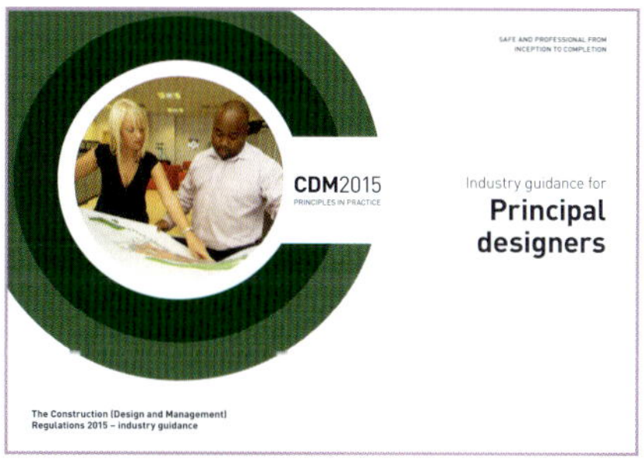

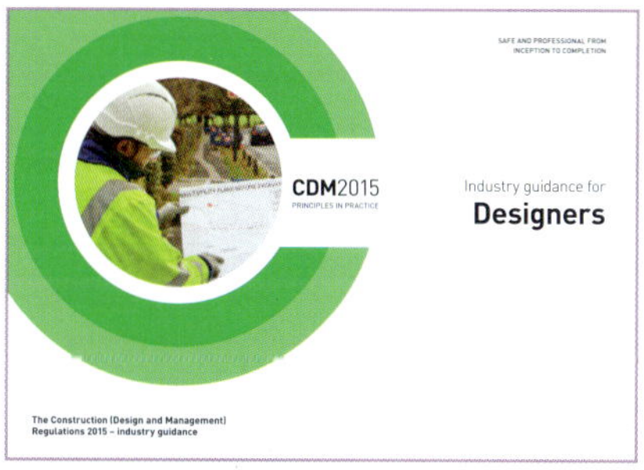

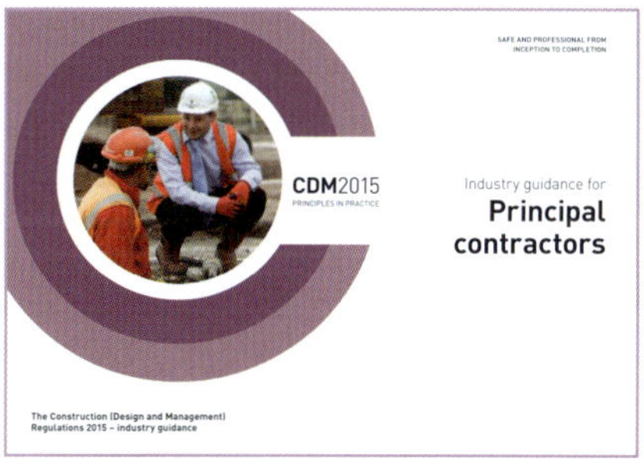

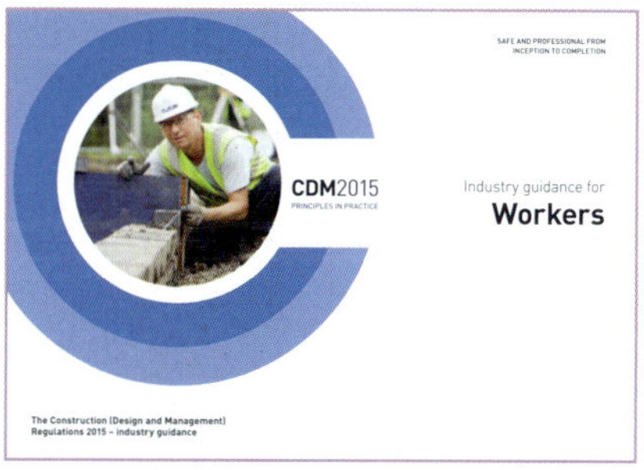

For a summary of the duty holders' main responsibilities refer to Appendix B.

www. **A free app 'CDM Wizard' has been produced by CITB to assist duty holders in complying with the regulations.**

3.3 Main elements to securing construction health and safety

The incorporation of the following elements into all construction projects is a requirement under CDM.

- ☑ Managing the risks to health and safety by applying the **general principles of prevention**.
- ☑ **Appointing** the right people and organisations at the right time.
- ☑ Ensuring everyone has the **information, instruction, training and supervision** necessary to enable them to carry out their jobs in a way that secures health and safety.
- ☑ Duty holders **co-operating and communicating** with them to promote and develop effective measures to secure health, safety and welfare.
- ☑ Consulting workers and engaging with them to promote and develop effective measures to secure health, safety and welfare.

A 03

3.3.1 General principles of prevention

Principal designers, designers, principal contractors and contractors must apply the principles of prevention when carrying out their duties and use these to identify control measures required to control the risks identified on the project.

The principles of prevention are the same for the CDM Regulations, as are included in Schedule 1 of the MHSW. These are listed below.

- ☑ Avoiding risks.
- ☑ Evaluating the risks that cannot be avoided.
- ☑ Combating the risks at source.
- ☑ Adapting the work to the individual, especially regarding the design of workplaces, the choice of work equipment and the choice of working and production methods, with a view, in particular, to alleviating monotonous work and work at a predetermined work rate and reducing their effect on health.
- ☑ Adapting to technical progress.
- ☑ Replacing the dangerous by the non-dangerous or the less dangerous.
- ☑ Developing a coherent overall prevention policy that covers technology, organisation of work, working conditions, social relationships and the influence of factors relating to the working environment.
- ☑ Giving collective protective measures priority over individual protective measures.
- ☑ Giving appropriate instructions to employees.

3.3.2 Appointing the right people and organisations at the right time

Anyone involved in the project must ensure they have the *skills, knowledge, training, experience* and, if they are an organisation the *organisational capability*, to carry out the work. This applies to those making the appointment, as well as those accepting the appointment.

Appointments for the project must be made as soon as practicable (for example, the principal designer should be appointed as early as possible). Failure for the client to make this appointment means that the client must fulfil the duties of the principal designer until such an appointment is made. Therefore, if the appointment is made late this could have a negative impact on the collation of data for the pre-construction information pack and design considerations may be overlooked, which could have an impact on the safety of the construction and residual maintenance requirements.

When appointing a designer or contractor reasonable steps should be made to ensure they understand how to identify the significant risks likely to arise during either design or construction. They should also be able to prevent those risks, or manage or control them to an acceptable level.

Pre-qualification questionnaires can be a useful tool. For example, the publicly available specification 91: *Construction related procurement – pre-qualification questionnaire* (PAS 91) includes health and safety questions, along with other matters (such as financial information).

For further information refer to Regulation 8 *General duties*. This regulation applies to anyone working on a project and includes workers as well as those with specific duties.

Failure to appoint the right people at the right time could have an impact on the health and safety performance and success of the project.

3.3.3 Supervision, instruction and information

Contractors and principal contractors must make sure that the supervision provided is effective and the required information is provided.

An assessment of the workforce's existing levels of skill, knowledge, training and experience, plus the health and safety risks involved in the project, needs to be made to ensure the correct level of supervision, instruction and information is provided. Other factors to consider to determine the correct level of supervision to be provided are the individual's age, agility, level of safety awareness, literacy and attitude.

Anyone with a duty under CDM to provide health and safety information or instructions must ensure they are easy to understand. For example, the information should be in clear English, or other languages, as appropriate for the people using it. The use of diagrams and pictures should also be considered and information should be proportionate to the scale and complexity of the risks.

Information about hazards is essential to all project workers and managers to ensure they understand the risks involved.

Instructions are actions that must be followed to prevent or minimise those risks.

3.3.4 Co-operating, communicating and co-ordinating

The regulations stipulate that duty holders must co-operate with other duty holders involved in the project or any project adjoining the site (Regulation 8(4)) and co-ordinate their work to ensure effective health and safety. They must also communicate with each other to ensure that everyone understands the risks, and the measures that need to be put into place to control those risks.

e.g.

Regulation 4 requires that the client takes reasonable steps to ensure that the principal designer and principal contractor comply with their duties, which include the requirement to plan, manage, monitor and co-ordinate their work.

There are many examples of where the various contractors involved in a project can co-operate, co-ordinate and communicate their work, agreeing who works where and when so that construction work runs smoothly and without the risks created by one set of workers endangering the health and safety of other workers. Daily briefings and project meetings are also good examples of achieving this.

3.3.5 Consulting and engaging with workers

Regulation 14 places a legal duty on principal contractors to consult and engage with workers.

Additionally, the **Safety Representatives and Safety Committee Regulations**, and the **Health and Safety (Consultation with Employees) Regulations** require employers to consult their workforce about health and safety.

Worker consultation and engagement is basically effective two-way communication between management and the workforce. It can help workers spot workplace risks and know what to do about them, ensure controls are effective and increase the worker's commitment to working in a safe and healthy way.

The following are requirements for the principal contractor.

- ☑ Make and maintain arrangements that will enable the principal contractor and the workers engaged in construction work to co-operate effectively in developing, promoting and checking the effectiveness of measures to ensure the health, safety and welfare of the workers.
- ☑ Consult with workers or their representatives in good time on matters connected with the project, which may affect their health, safety or welfare.
- ☑ Ensure that workers or their representatives can inspect and take copies of any information that the principal contractor has, or which these regulations require to be provided to the principal contractor, which relate to the health, safety or welfare of workings at the site. There are a number of exceptions to this requirement, which are detailed in Regulation 14(c)(i-v).

Encouragement and ample opportunity must be given for all members of the workforce to feed back to management any concerns that they might have regarding health and safety. It is the workforce who have first-hand experience of actually carrying out the job and who may therefore be more knowledgeable about the risks involved.

Depending upon the circumstances, consultation might be carried out directly with a single worker, groups of workers or through health and safety representatives, whether trade union-appointed or not.

www.

The HSE website hosts the leadership and worker involvement toolkit (LWIT), which aims to help contractors and managers learn how to make health and safety improvements in their business.

3.4 The regulations

The CDM Regulations place responsibility for managing the health and safety of a construction project on the many duty holders.

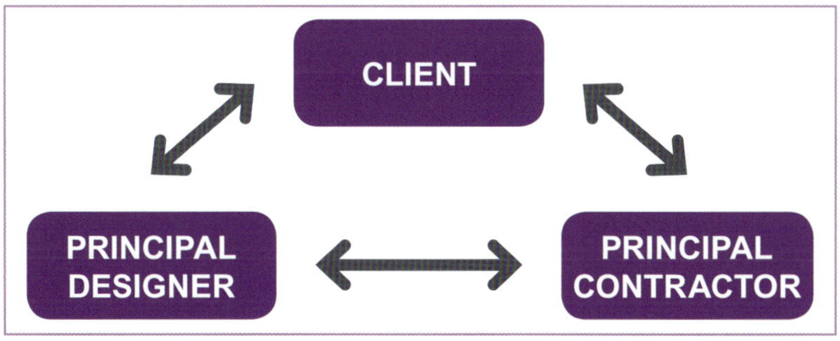

The **client** must ensure that suitable arrangements are made, reviewed and maintained to manage the health and safety risks involved in the project. For projects involving more than one contractor the regulations require the client to appoint a principal designer and principal contractor and to make sure they carry out their duties.

The **principal designer** is required to plan, manage, monitor and co-ordinate the work during the pre-construction phase. They must also liaise with the principal contractor to provide them with the relevant information for planning, management and monitoring during the construction phase.

The main duty of the **principal contractor** is to plan, manage, monitor and co-ordinate the work during the construction phase. They must also liaise with the client and principal designer throughout the project, including during the pre-construction phase.

Depending on the nature of the project the principal designer and principal contractor may be supported by **designers, contractors** and **workers**.

There are three important phases of the project, known as the pre-construction phase, the construction phase and the post-construction phase.

The **pre-construction phase** covers the inception, design and planning stage of a project (before the construction or building work starts), although it is acknowledged that design and planning continues into the construction phase. Data for the *pre-construction information* will be collated during this stage.

The **construction phase** runs from start to finish of the construction or building work. The *construction phase plan* will be followed during this stage.

The **post-construction phase** is the practical completion of the construction or building work, including handover. The *health and safety file* will be completed and handed over during this stage.

A project is notifiable if the construction work is likely to be more than 30 days and have more than 20 workers working simultaneously or exceed 500 person days.

The following parts of the regulations apply to the whole construction process, from concept to completion.

Part 1	Introduction.	**Schedule 1**	Particulars to be notified under Regulation 6.
Part 2	Client duties.	**Schedule 2**	Welfare facilities.
Part 3	Health and safety duties and roles.	**Schedule 3**	Work involving particular risks.
Part 5	General.		

Parts 1, 2, 3 and 5 of the CDM Regulations cover the whole construction project, from concept to completion.

Part 4 sets out a number of provisions that only apply to work carried out on the construction site.

Unlike the CDM Regulations 2007, where only Part 2 or Part 4 applied to all construction work, all regulations now apply to a project (except for Part 4).

Where there is more than one contractor, or it is reasonably foreseeable that more than one contractor will be working on the project at any time, the client needs to appoint, in writing, a principal designer and principal contractor and ensure that a construction phase plan is prepared. **These appointments must be made regardless of whether a project is notifiable or not.**

Every construction project or building job, no matter how small, is a CDM job. The requirements of CDM 2015 apply regardless of whether the project is notifiable or not.

The requirement for duty holders to have the skills, knowledge, training and experience or, where they are an organisation the organisational capability, and the arrangements for the co-ordination of work and co-operation between all those working on the project **applies to all projects**.

For Schedule 2, Welfare facilities, of the CDM Regulations refer to Appendix D.

For definitions, in accordance with the CDM Regulations, refer to Appendix A.

A 03

3.5 Notification (Form F10)

A project is notifiable by the client when it is scheduled to last longer than 30 working days and have more than 20 workers working simultaneously at any point in the project or exceed 500 person days. A day is taken as being eight hours work and a working day is where work is planned. **If there is a major change that will result in a significant delay or change to the project itself, the work could become notifiable at a later date.**

Holidays and weekends do not count if construction work is not carried out at those times.

A *person day* is the number of hours worked by an individual and includes any shift work. In any one working day, where shift work takes place, there will be more than one person day in the working day. A person day also includes any other length of time worked that is less than one full day.

A notifiable project

The responsibility of the designers and contractors to ensure that the client is aware of their CDM duties is vitally important to this. As construction professionals they are in the best place to advise on the planned timescales. Clients must ensure an up to date copy of the notice is displayed on the construction site and it can be easily understood, taking into consideration workers where English may not be their first language. The client can do this themselves or ask the principal contractor or contractor to do so.

The notice to the relevant enforcing authority must be in writing. The enforcing authority could be the **HSE**, the **Office of Rail Regulation**, or the **Office for Nuclear Regulation**. Details of the information required for the notification are given in Schedule 1 of CDM 2015 and include details such as the planned start date, contact details of the duty holders and the planned number of contractors on the site.

The easiest way to notify any project is on an electronic F10 form. The online system also allows the retrieval, amendment and re-submission of previously completed F10 forms.

www.

The F10 form can be downloaded from the CDM section of the HSE website.

The notification must be sent as soon as practicable before the construction phase begins. If not all of the details are known at that time, as much detail as possible must be sent and the remaining details forwarded as soon as they become known.

Where the client is a domestic client the duty to notify can be carried out by either the contractor (if there is only one contractor), the principal contractor (where there is more than one contractor) or the principal designer (where there is a written agreement that the principal designer will fulfil the client's duties).

3.6 Duty holders

3.6.1 Client

Clients

- ☑ A **client** is any person for whom a project is carried out.
- ☑ A **commercial client** is organisations or individuals for whom a construction project is being carried out in connection with a business, whether the business operates for profit or not.
- ☑ A **domestic client** is a client for whom a project is being carried out, which is not in the course or furtherance of a business of that client.

The term *client* includes both domestic clients and commercial clients. However, Regulation 7 limits the way in which CDM 2015 applies to a domestic client.

Clients have an important role in the construction process. The regulations make them accountable for the impact that their decisions and approach has on health, safety and welfare of those working on the project, plus anyone who may be affected by those project activities. The client has contractual control, makes appointments and determines the money, time and resources available for the project.

Where it is not clear who the client is, due to a number of individuals and organisations involved, then Regulation 4(8) allows all the possible clients to elect one or more person(s) to be treated as the client. When deciding who this could be consideration should be given to who:

- ☑ decides what is constructed where, when and by whom
- ☑ commissions the design and construction work
- ☑ initiates the work
- ☑ is at the head of the procurement chain
- ☑ appoints contractors (including the principal contractor) and designers (including the principal designer).

If a commercial client fails to appoint either a principal designer or a principal contractor they must fulfill those duties themselves, until an appointment has been made.

Further details of client duties can be found in the legal (L) series and industry guidance, but are summarised below.

Summary of client duties

Commercial client	Domestic client
■ Make arrangements to manage the project without risk to health and safety. ■ Ensure welfare arrangements are provided, as detailed in Schedule 2. ■ Allow sufficient time and resources for all stages. ■ Provide pre-construction information to designers and contractors as soon as possible. ■ Ensure, before the construction phase begins, a construction plan is drawn up by the principal contractor, or the contractor if there is only one contractor. ■ Ensure the principal designer prepares the health and safety file for the project. ■ Take reasonable steps to ensure the principal designer and principal contractor comply with their duties. ■ If the client's interest in the structure changes, they must pass the health and safety file onto their successor, making sure they are aware of the contents of the file. ■ Ensure those they appoint have the skills, knowledge, training, experience and capabilities to carry out those roles.	■ Where there is one contractor the client's duties must be carried out by the contractor. ■ Where there is more than one contractor the client's duties must be carried out by the principal contractor. ■ Domestic clients can have a written agreement to transfer their client duties to the principal designer. If this happens, the principal contractor will work to the principal designer as the client. ■ Where there is more than one contractor a principal contractor and principal designer should be appointed. ■ If the domestic client fails to appoint a designer, the designer in control of the pre-construction phase becomes the designer. ■ If the domestic client fails to appoint a contractor, the contractor in control of the construction phase is the principal contractor.

www.

For further information on working for a domestic client refer to Appendix 5 of the legal (L) series guidance.

For further information refer to the industry guidance for clients.

3.6.2 Principal designer

Principal designer

The principal designer is the designer with control over the pre-construction phase of the project. They are appointed by the client.

Principal designers are responsible for influencing how the health and safety risks should be controlled and incorporated into the project's delivery. They must plan, manage, monitor and co-ordinate matters relating to health and safety during the pre-construction phase to ensure that the project is carried out without risks to health or safety, taking into account the principles of prevention. Principal designers are designers appointed by the client. They must consider their own skills, knowledge, training, experience and, where they are an organisation, they must also consider their organisational capabilities and seek advice where required. They may also have separate duties as a designer.

Further details of principal designers' duties can be found in the legal (L) series and industry guidance, but are summarised on the following page.

Summary of principal designer duties

- Plan, manage, monitor and co-ordinate the pre-construction phase.
- Co-ordinate matters relating to health and safety during the pre-construction phase.
- Estimate the period of time required to complete work stages.
- Take account of the general principles of prevention.
- Identify, eliminate or control foreseeable risks to health and safety of any person carrying out construction work, maintaining or cleaning a structure and/or using a structure designed as a workplace.
- Ensure designers comply with their duties.
- Ensure all persons co-operate with the client, principal designer and each other.
- Assist the client in the provision of the pre-construction information.
- Provide pre-construction information promptly and in a convenient form to every designer or contractor.
- Liaise with the principal contractor and share information relevant to the planning, management and monitoring of the construction phase and the co-ordination of health and safety during construction.
- Review, update and complete the health and safety file and pass to the client upon completion.
- Hand over the health and safety file to the principal contractor if their appointment finishes before the end of the project.

For further information refer to the industry guidance for principal designers.

3.6.3 Designer

Designer

A designer is an organisation or individual who prepares or modifies a design for a construction project (including the design of temporary works) or arranges for or instructs someone else to do so.

Designers are in a unique position at an early stage of a project to reduce the potential risks to health and safety that could arise during the construction phase or at a later stage (such as during maintenance of the completed structure). Therefore, designers should address health and safety issues from the outset. If designers fail to consider health and safety at an early stage this could result in delays to the project and could cause problems during the construction phase, as contractors will need to identify ways to undertake the work safely.

Further details of designers' duties can be found in the legal (L) series and industry guidance, but are summarised below. These duties become applicable as soon as a design has been prepared, which may be used for construction work. It is irrelevant if planning permission and funds have not yet been secured.

Designers have the same duties when working for a domestic client as they do when working for a commercial client.

Summary of designer duties

- Must not commence work unless they are satisfied that the client is aware of their duties.
- Eliminate hazards and reduce risks during design.
- Provide information about remaining risks to the principal designer and ensure information is in the health and safety file.
- Take into account the principles of prevention when preparing or modifying a design.
- Eliminate health and safety risks that may affect those carrying out future construction work, maintaining or cleaning a structure or using a structure designed as a workplace.
- Take steps to reduce any residual risks through the design process.
- Supply information to the client, other designers and contractors, so they can comply with their duties.
- The same duties apply to designers for designs that are prepared or modified outside of Great Britain.

For further information refer to the industry guidance for designers.

For an example of CDM RAG lists refer to Appendix C.

3.6.4 Principal contractor

Principal contractor

A principal contractor is the organisation or person who co-ordinates the work of the construction phase of the project involving more than one contractor, so that it is carried out in a way that secures health and safety.

A principal contractor is appointed by the client and they and anyone they appoint must have the skills, knowledge, training, experience and, where they are an organisation the organisational capability, to carry out their work in a way that secures health and safety. The principal contractor must ensure the principles of prevention are taken into account. They must plan, manage, monitor and co-ordinate the construction phase to ensure that construction work is carried out without risks to health and safety.

Plan

- ☑ Take into account risks to workers, members of the public and clients' employees.
- ☑ Consider risks likely to arise during construction.
- ☑ Provide the right level of supervision, necessary information, instruction and training.

Manage

- ☑ Ensure those engaged to carry out the work are capable.
- ☑ Put preventative and protective measures in place.
- ☑ Provide the right plant, equipment and tools.
- ☑ Demonstrate good leadership.
- ☑ Ensure workers understand the risks and control measures, and who has responsibility for health and safety.
- ☑ Investigate incidents so that lessons can be learnt.

Good supervision is part of showing good leadership in health and safety.

Monitor

- ☑ Check standards regularly, taking into account the rapidly changing construction environment, and allocate sufficient time and effort for this.
- ☑ Treat health and safety in the same way as other important business aspects.
- ☑ Take prompt action.
- ☑ Use both active and reactive monitoring.

Active monitoring includes routine checks of areas, plant and equipment, or health risk management to prevent harm.

Reactive monitoring includes investigating near-miss incidents, injuries and monitoring ill health cases.

Co-ordinate

- ☑ Ensure contractors co-operate with each other.
- ☑ Apply the general principles of prevention.
- ☑ Follow the construction phase plan.
- ☑ Liaise with those on site so they understand the health and safety standards expected and gain their co-operation.
- ☑ Work with the client to ensure co-ordination of contractors on neighbouring sites.

There should only be one principal contractor for a project at any one time. Their role, when working on a project for a domestic client, is no different to the role undertaken for a commercial client.

Summary of principal contractor duties
■ Plan, manage, monitor and co-ordinate the construction phase plan. ■ Estimate the time required to complete the work. ■ Take into account the general principles of prevention. ■ Organise co-operation between contractors. ■ Comply with the health and safety legal requirements. ■ Ensure the construction phase plan is followed. ■ Provide suitable site induction. ■ Prevent unauthorised access to the site. ■ Provide welfare facilities. ■ Liaise with the principal designer. ■ Consult and engage with workers. ■ Review, update and complete the health and safety file, if the principal designer's appointment finishes before the end of the project.

For further information refer to the industry guidance for principal contractors.

3.6.5 Contractor

Contractor

A contractor is anyone who directly employs or engages construction workers or manages construction. A contractor can be an individual, sole trader, self-employed worker or a business that carries out, manages or controls construction work as part of their business.

A contractor must plan, manage and monitor how the construction work is carried out, either by the contractor or by the workers under the contractor's control. If a contractor gets involved in any design work (such as temporary work or design of a hot air system) they could also have duties as designers.

The duties on contractors apply whether the workers under their control are employees, self-employed or agency workers.

All contractors, including, for example, utility companies, specialist contractors and the self-employed, have a part to play in ensuring health and safety on site, via the proper co-ordination of their work, underpinned by effective communication and co-operation.

Summary of contractor duties
■ Check that the client is aware of their duties. ■ Plan, manage and monitor construction work. ■ If there is only one contractor on site, that contractor must take into account the principles of prevention, estimate the time required to complete the project and draw up the construction phase plan. ■ Comply with directions given by the principal designer or principal contractor. ■ Comply with the construction phase plan. ■ Consult workers who are their employees. ■ Appoint workers who have, or are in the process of obtaining, the necessary skills, knowledge, training and experience to carry out the tasks that have been allocated. ■ Provide supervision, as required, depending on the hazards, risks, skills, knowledge, training and experience of the individuals. ■ Provide information and instruction. ■ Provide a site induction (if not already provided by the principal contractor). ■ Prevent unauthorised access to site. ■ Provide welfare facilities for their own employees who are working on the site or anyone else working under their control. ■ Contractors appointed by the client (such as those on term contracts) are under the control of the principal contractor for the purposes of planning, managing and monitoring the construction work.

Contractors have the same duties when working for a domestic client as they do when working for a commercial client.

For further information refer to the industry guidance for contractors.

3.7 Workers

CDM recognises the importance of workers. It helps managers and workers to work together to improve health and safety, which will result in fewer construction workers suffering fatal injuries, becoming injured and/or suffering from ill health.

Employers, contractors and principal contractors should provide workers with the following.

- ☑ Health and safety information.
- ☑ Site induction, which covers site familiarisation and orientation (not just training).
- ☑ The necessary health and safety training, consultation and engagement.
- ☑ A respected and trusted workplace health and safety culture.
- ☑ Appropriate supervision, relevant to the work activities being carried out and the skills, knowledge and training.
- ☑ A safe place to work by managing hazards and communicating those control measures to workers.
- ☑ An explanation of the arrangements for co-operation and co-ordination.
- ☑ Adequate clean and accessible welfare facilities for men and women.

Where English is not the worker's first language, in order for contractors to fulfil their duties they could consider translating the site rules, using interpreters for inductions and task briefings, or replacing written notices with symbols or diagrams.

For further information refer to the industry guidance for workers.

3.8 Project documents

With regard to project documentation, CDM requires the creation of a construction phase plan and a health and safety file.

Furthermore, the regulations require that relevant pre-construction information is gathered and compiled to form the basis of the construction phase plan for all projects. This must include all the project-specific information that is relevant to health and safety during the construction.

3.8.1 Pre-construction information

Pre-construction information provides health and safety information needed by designers and contractors, who are bidding for work on the project or who have already been appointed, to enable them to carry out their duties. It also provides information to the principal designers and principal contractors in planning, managing, monitoring and co-ordinating the work of the project, and it will form the basis of the construction phase plan.

It is the client's duty to provide pre-construction information. For projects where there is more than one contractor the client should expect the principal designer to help them bring the pre-construction information together, help them identify what must be obtained and provide it to the designers and contractors.

The client or principal designer may have to approach other organisations (such as utility companies or asbestos surveyors) to gather some of the information required.

Information for the file must:

- ☑ be relevant to the project
- ☑ have the appropriate level of detail
- ☑ be proportionate given the health and safety risks involved.

Where the client has created a useful pack of information, the tendering contractors' responses to questions asked can be used as part of the client checks to ensure that people and organisations appointed have the necessary skills, knowledge and experience and, if an organisation the organisational capability, to manage the health and safety risks.

For a copy of the suggested contents list for pre-construction information refer to Section G: *Checklists and forms*.

3.8.2 Construction phase plan

The construction phase plan must record the following information.

- Health and safety arrangements for the construction phase.
- Site rules.
- Specific control measures where a worker could be put at risk (as detailed in Schedule 3 of CDM 2015).

Information included in the plan must:

- be relevant to the project
- have sufficient detail to set out the arrangements, site rules and special measures needed to manage the construction phase
- be proportionate to the scale and complexity of the project and risks involved.

The client must ensure the construction phase plan is drawn up **before** the construction phase begins. For projects involving more than one contractor the principal contractor is responsible for drawing up the plan. For single contractor projects the contractor is responsible. The principal designer must help the principal contractor to prepare the plan by providing any relevant information that they hold.

As the project develops it is likely that the construction phase plan will be amended and further developed in the light of emerging issues and situations. It is a live working document that is the basis for the effective health and safety management of the project.

The principal contractor or contractor are responsible for the following.

- Preparing a construction phase plan, before the start of the construction phase, which is sufficient to ensure that the construction phase is planned, managed and monitored in such a way that construction work can be carried out without risk to health or safety, so far as is reasonably practicable, paying adequate regard to the pre-construction information provided by the designers.
- Throughout the project, reviewing, revising and refining the plan as often as is appropriate, so that it continues to be sufficient to fulfil the above requirement.
- Arranging for the plan to be implemented in such a way as to ensure, so far as is reasonably practicable, the health and safety of all persons carrying out construction work and other persons who may be affected by it.

Generally, during the construction phase, the construction phase plan will be expanded to outline the following.

- Details of the arrangements for protecting the health and safety of all persons who may be affected in any way by the construction work.
- Arrangements for the monitoring of the health and safety performance of persons involved in construction work to ensure they are complying with relevant statutory provisions and the health and safety plan.
- Information concerning the welfare arrangements that have been made.

Relevant parts of the information contained in the construction phase plan must be made available to, or be made known to, contractors before construction commences, so that they may be aware of risks to health and safety that may arise for their employees.

With this knowledge they will be able to meet the requirements that are imposed on them under the construction phase plan. They obviously also have to meet the requirements that are imposed on them by the relevant statutory provisions.

For an example of a construction phase plan refer to Section G: *Checklists and forms.*

3.8.3 Health and safety file

The purpose of the health and safety file is to ensure that, at the end of the project, the client has information about the health and safety risks that anyone carrying out subsequent construction work on the building will need to know about.

The client must ensure that the principal designer prepares the health and safety file and it is revised, as appropriate, and kept available for inspection by any person who may need to refer to it to obtain necessary information to undertake the work safely. This means that the role involves selecting relevant information to include, and possibly rejecting other material that is submitted. For example, putting the construction phase method statements about groundworks in the file is unlikely to be useful in the future, whereas identifying the position and size of the crane used for lifting in steelwork or air-conditioning units may be of use. If the role of the principal designer finishes before the end of the project, the client should ensure that the file is handed to the principal contractor.

The emphasis is on information that has a relevance to the future.

At the completion of the project, the file is given to the client and, unless further changes to the structure are made, it then remains as a permanent record of how the project was designed and built.

For a suggested contents list for the health and safety file refer to Section G: *Checklists and forms*.

3.9 General requirements for all construction sites

Part 4 of the regulations sets out a number of provisions (listed below) that only relate to construction work carried out on a construction site.

- ☑ Applies only to a construction site.
- ☑ Requires a contractor to comply with the requirements of this part.
- ☑ Requires a domestic client, who controls the way in which construction work is carried out, to comply with the requirements of this part, so far as they relate to matters within the client's control.

The following duties in the table apply to all construction sites, regardless of size, nature or duration.

Regulation number and title	Details of duties and requirements
16. Application of Regulations 17 to 35.	This regulation states that every contractor carrying out construction work must comply.
17. Safe places of work.	Every place of work must be safe to access, egress and to work at, and unauthorised access must be prevented, and sufficient working space must be provided.
18. Good order and site security.	Sites must be tidy, secure (to prevent unauthorised access), have appropriate signs and have no projecting sharp objects.
19. Stability of structures.	Buildings and structures must not be allowed to become unstable during work and any supports provided must be adequate for the job.
20. Demolition or dismantling.	This work must be carried out so as to prevent any danger and there must be a written plan (for example method statement) in place before work starts.
21. Explosives.	Explosives must be stored, transported and used safely. Steps must be taken to ensure persons are not exposed to risk of injury from the explosion or the projected or flying material.
22. Excavations.	Work in excavations must be properly planned. They must not be allowed to collapse or have materials falling or slipping into them. No-one should become trapped because of inadequate shoring. Excavations must be inspected and reports written as appropriate. Work in an excavation must not start where an inspection has revealed that it is not safe to do so.
23. Cofferdams and caissons.	Cofferdams and caissons must be suitably designed, constructed, maintained and inspected. Cofferdams and caissons must be inspected by a competent person at the start of every shift or if the strength or stability has been affected. If the inspection reveals it is not safe then work must not start until this has been rectified.
24. Reports of inspections.	The duty to carry out inspections refers to Regulations 22 and 23 and requires inspections to be made at the start of every shift and after any event likely to affect the safety of the excavation, cofferdam or caisson. The person carrying out the inspection must inform the person on whose behalf the inspection was carried out, before the end of the shift, any health and safety risks identified. A written record of an inspection must be made at intervals not exceeding seven days. It must be retained until completion of the project and then for a further three months.
25. Energy distribution installations.	Energy distribution installations must be located, checked and indicated. Overhead power cables must be protected against being damaged or causing injury or damage. Work must not take place where there is a risk of damage to, or accidental disturbance of, energy distribution systems, unless suitable control measures have been taken.
26. Prevention of drowning.	Where there is risk of a person drowning because of falling into water or other liquid, suitable measures must be put in place to prevent falls and, where a risk remains, minimise the risk of drowning and ensure there is a rescue plan and maintained equipment in place. Where workers are transported over water to and from their place of work, the vessel must not be overcrowded or overloaded.
27. Traffic routes.	Traffic routes must be organised to protect people from injury from vehicles and be suitable for the number of vehicles and persons using them. Traffic routes must be properly maintained, suitably signed and regularly inspected. Where it is unsafe for pedestrians to use gates intended for use by vehicles, separate pedestrian gates must be provided, marked and kept free of obstruction.

Regulation number and title	Details of duties and requirements
28. Vehicles.	Arrangements must be made to prevent unintended movement of any vehicle. They must be used safely, not overloaded and prevented from falling into any excavation. No-one must be allowed to ride on any vehicle unless it is designed to carry passenger(s) and it is safe to do so. No-one must remain on any vehicle that is being loaded unless a safe place is provided and maintained on the vehicle.
29. Prevention of risk from fire, flooding, and so on.	Steps must be taken to avoid the risk of fire, explosion, flooding and asphyxiation from any substance.
30. Emergency procedures.	A plan must be in place for the safe evacuation of all people on site in situations where there is a foreseeable risk of an emergency. Everyone on site must be made aware of the emergency plan and it must be practised at suitable intervals.
31. Emergency routes and exits.	Adequate means of evacuation (emergency escape routes) to a safe place must be established. Routes must be kept clear of obstruction and be adequately signed.
32. Fire detection and fire-fighting.	Suitable fire-fighting equipment, fire detection equipment and alarms must be provided, examined and tested at suitable intervals and suitably located. Manual fire-fighting equipment (such as hand-held extinguishers), must be easy to access and indicated by appropriate signs. An appropriate number of on-site staff must be trained in the use of fire-fighting equipment.
33. Fresh air.	Places of construction work or on the approach to construction work must have adequate fresh or purified air available. Where fresh or purified air is provided by plant, it must be equipped with suitable audible or visible warnings to indicate any inadequacy in the supply or machine failure.
34. Temperature and weather protection.	Steps must be taken to ensure that indoor temperatures are reasonable. Outdoor workplaces must be arranged to provide adequate protection against adverse weather, taking into account usage and protective clothing or equipment provided.
35. Lighting.	Every place of work, its access and egress routes and any traffic route must be adequately lit, preferably by natural light. Where lighting is by artificial means, a back-up system must be in place where failure of the primary system would result in risks to health or safety. Artificial light must not adversely affect or change the perception of any health and safety sign or signal.

A
03

Appendix A – Definitions (Regulation 2)

Design. Includes drawings, design details, specifications, bills of quantities (including specification of articles or substances) relating to a structure, and calculations prepared for the purpose of a design.

Construction work. Carrying out any building, civil engineering or engineering construction work, such as those listed below.

- ☑ Construction, alteration, conversion, fitting out, commissioning, renovation, repair, upkeep, redecoration or other maintenance (including cleaning, that involves using water on an abrasive at high pressure), cleaning (using corrosive or toxic substances), decommissioning, demolition or dismantling of a structure.
- ☑ Preparatory works for an intended structure, including site clearance, exploration, investigation (but not site survey) and excavation (but not pre-archaeological investigations), and clearance of preparation of the site or structure for use of occupation at its conclusion.
- ☑ Assembly on site of prefabricated elements to form a structure or the disassembly on site of the prefabricated elements, which immediately before disassembly formed such a structure.
- ☑ Removal of a structure or of any product or waste resulting from demolition or dismantling of a structure from disassembly or prefabricated elements, which immediately before such disassembly formed such a structure.
- ☑ Installation, commissioning, maintenance, repair or removal of mechanical, electrical, gas, compressed air, hydraulic, telecommunications, computer or similar services, which are normally fixed within or to a structure.

Structure. This means any building, timber, masonry, metal or reinforced concrete structure, railway line or siding, tramway line, dock, harbour, inland navigation, tunnel, shaft, bridge, viaduct, waterworks, reservoir, pipe or pipeline, cable, aqueduct, sewer, sewerage works, gas holder, road, airfield, sea defence work, river work, drainage work, earthwork, lagoon, dam, wall, caisson, mast, tower, pylon, underground tank, earth retaining structure or structure designed to preserve or alter any natural feature, fixed plant and any structure similar to those listed, or formwork, falsework, scaffold or other structure designed or used to provide support or means of access during construction work. *(**Note:** any reference to a structure includes part of a structure.)*

Project. A project which includes or is intended to include construction work, including planning, design, management or other work involved in a project until the end of the construction phase.

Notifiable project. Specific details of the project have to be notified to the relevant enforcing authority or Office of Nuclear Regulation by the client as soon as practicable before the construction phase begins. A project is notifiable if the construction work on a construction site is scheduled to last longer than 30 working days and have more than 20 workers working simultaneously at any point in the project or exceed 500 person days.

The **construction phase** starts when construction work on the project commences, and ends when construction work in that project is completed.

Client. A client may be a single person or an organisation. They are the people for whom the work is being carried out. They have duties under CDM when a project is commissioned in connection with a business activity, even if it is commissioned by a not-for-profit organisation. Whether or not the client's duties apply will be obvious on many occasions, but may require some delicate questioning of the client by the designer, contractor or others.

Domestic client. A person who has construction work carried out in their own home, or the home of a family member, which is not done as part of a business, whether for profit or not. A domestic client can transfer their duties to a contractor, principal contractor or principal designer. Regulation 7 limits the way in which the regulations apply to domestic clients.

Principal designer. The person appointed by the client on projects that have more than one contractor. This can be an individual or an organisation with sufficient knowledge, experience and ability to carry out the role for the construction project.

Designer. Any person who whilst at work (whether they are paid or not) carries out any design work, including modification, or arranges for someone under their control to do design work.

Principal contractor. The contractor appointed by the client. Their most important duties are to co-ordinate and manage the construction phase of the project, and ensure the health and safety of everyone involved in the construction work or anyone who may be affected by it.

Contractor. Can be an individual or a company who are completing the actual construction work.

Appendix B – Summary of duty holders' roles and duties under CDM 2015

CDM duty holders	Legal definition	Who are they?	Summary of role/main duty
Clients	Any person for whom a project is carried out.	Organisations or individuals for whom a construction project is carried out.	Make suitable arrangements for managing a project. This includes making sure: ■ other duty holders are appointed ■ sufficient time and resources are allocated ■ relevant information is prepared and provided to other duty holders ■ the principal designer and principal contractor carry out their duties ■ welfare facilities are provided.
Domestic clients	Client for whom a project is being carried out, which is not in the course of furtherance of a business of that client.	People who have construction work carried out on their own home, or the home of a family member that is not done as part of a business, whether for profit or not.	Their duties as a client are normally transferred to either: ■ the contractor on a single contractor project, or ■ the principal contractor, on a project involving more than one contractor. However the domestic client can choose to have a written agreement with the principal designer to carry out the client duties.
Designers	Any person (including a client, contractor or other person referred to in the regulations) who, in the course of furtherance of business: ■ prepares or modifies a design, or ■ arranges for or instructs any person under their control to do so relating to a structure or to a product or mechanical or electrical system intended for a particular structure, and a person is deemed to prepare a design where a design is prepared by a person under their control.	Those who, as part of a business, prepare or modify designs for a building, product or system relating to construction work.	When preparing or modifying designs, to eliminate, reduce or control foreseeable risks that may arise during: ■ construction, and ■ the maintenance and use of a building once it is built. Provide information to other members of the project team to help them fulfil their duties.
Principal designers	The designer appointed under Regulation 5(1)(a) to perform specified duties in Regulations 11 and 12.	Designers appointed by the client in projects involving more than one contractor. They can be an organisation or an individual with sufficient knowledge, experience and ability to carry out the role.	Plan, manage, monitor and co-ordinate health and safety in the pre-construction phase of a project. This includes: ■ identifying, eliminating and controlling foreseeable risks ■ ensuring designers carry out their duties. Prepare and provide relevant information to other duty holders. Liaise with the principal contractor to help in the planning, management, monitoring and co-ordination of the construction phase.

A 03

CDM duty holders	Legal definition	Who are they?	Summary of role/main duty
Principal contractors	The contractors appointed under Regulation 5(1)(b) to perform specified duties in Regulations 11 and 12.	Contractors appointed by the client to co-ordinate the construction phase of a project where it involves more than one contractor.	Plan, manage, monitor and co-ordinate the construction phase of a project. This includes: ▪ liaising with the client and principal designer ▪ preparing the construction phase plan ▪ organising co-operation between contractors and co-ordinating their work. Ensure the following. ▪ Suitable site inductions are provided. ▪ Reasonable steps are taken to prevent unauthorised access. ▪ Workers are consulted and engaged in securing their health and safety. ▪ Welfare facilities are provided.
Contractors	Any person (including a non-domestic client) who, in the course of furtherance of business, carries out, manages or controls construction work.	Those who do the actual construction work and can be either an individual or a company.	Plan, manage and monitor construction work under their control so that it is carried out without risks to health and safety. For projects involving more than one contractor, co-ordinate their activities with others in the project team – in particular, comply with directions given to them by the principal designer or principal contractor. For single contractor projects, prepare a construction phase plan.
Workers (Not duty holders, but an integral part of CDM.)	N/A	The people who work for or under the control of contractors on a construction site.	They must: ▪ be consulted about matters that affect their health, safety and welfare ▪ take care of their own health and safety and that of others who may be affected by their actions ▪ report anything they see that is likely to endanger their own or others' health and safety ▪ co-operate with their employer, fellow workers, contractors and other duty holders.

(Reproduced from the Construction (Design and Management) Regulations 2015 Draft 'L series' guidance book.)

Appendix C – CDM RAG lists

The HSE has produced CDM red, amber and green (RAG) lists. These are practical aids for designers on what to eliminate or avoid and what to encourage. An example is shown below.

Red lists
Hazardous procedures, products and processes that should be eliminated from the project where possible.

- Lack of adequate pre-construction information (such as asbestos surveys, details of geology, obstructions, services and ground contamination).
- Hand scabbling of concrete (such as stop ends).
- Demolition by hand-held breakers of the top sections of concrete piles (pile cropping techniques are available).
- Specification of fragile roof lights and roofing assemblies.
- Processes giving rise to large quantities of dust (such as dry cutting and blasting).
- On-site spraying of harmful substances.
- Specification of structural steelwork that is not purposely designed to accommodate safety nets.
- Designing roof mounted services requiring access (for maintenance and so on), without provision for safe access (such as barriers).
- Glazing that cannot be accessed safely. All glazing should be anticipated as requiring cleaning and replacement, so a safe system of access is essential.
- Entrances, floors, ramps, stairs and escalators, not specifically designed to avoid slips and trips during use and maintenance, including taking into account the effect of rain water and spillages.
- Design of environments involving adverse lighting, noise, vibration, temperature, wetness, humidity and draughts or chemical and/or biological conditions during use and maintenance operations.
- Designs of structures that do not allow for fire containment during construction.

Amber lists
Products, processes and procedures to be eliminated or reduced as far as possible and only specified or allowed if unavoidable. Including amber items would always lead to the provision of information to the principal contractor.

- Internal manholes and inspection chambers in circulation areas.
- External manholes in heavily used vehicle access zones.
- Specification of 'lip' details (such as trip hazards) at the tops of pre-cast concrete staircases.
- Specification of small steps (such as risers) in external paved areas.
- Specification of heavy building blocks (those weighing > 20 kgs).
- Large and heavy glass panels.
- Chasing out concrete, brick or blockwork walls or floors for the installation of services.
- Specification of heavy lintels (the use of slim metal or hollow concrete lintels are better alternatives).
- Specification of solvent-based paints and thinners, or isocyanates, particularly for use in confined areas.
- Specification of curtain wall or panel systems without provision for tying or raking of scaffolds.
- Specification of blockwork walls > 3.5 metres high using retarded mortar mixes.
- Site traffic routes that do not allow for one-way systems and/or vehicular traffic segregated from site personnel.
- Site layout that does not allow adequate room for delivery and/or storage of materials, including site specific components.
- Heavy construction components that cannot be handled using mechanical lifting devices (because of access restrictions/floor loading and so on).
- On-site welding, in particular for new structures.
- Use of large piling rigs and cranes near live railways and overhead electric power lines or where proximity to obstructions prevents guarding of rigs.

Green lists

Products, processes and procedures to be positively encouraged.

- Adequate access for construction vehicles to minimise reversing requirements (one-way systems and turning radii).
- Provision of adequate access and headroom for maintenance in plant rooms, and adequate provision for replacing heavy components.
- Thoughtful location of mechanical and electrical equipment, light fittings, security devices, and so on to facilitate access, and placed away from crowded areas.
- Specification of concrete products with pre-cast fixings to avoid drilling.
- Specification of half board sizes for plasterboard sheets to make handling easier.
- Early installation of permanent means of access, and prefabricated staircases with handrails.
- Provision of edge protection at permanent works where there is a forseeable risk of falls after handover.
- Practical and safe methods of window cleaning (for example, from the inside).
- Appointment of a temporary works co-ordinator (BS 5975).
- Off-site timber treatment if PPA- and CCA-based preservatives are used (boron or copper salts can be used for cut ends on site).
- Off-site fabrication and prefabricated elements to minimise on-site hazards.
- Encourage the use of engineering controls to minimise the use of personal protective equipment.

Appendix D – Schedule 2 Welfare facilities

Regulations 4(2)(b), 13(4)(c) and 15(11).

1. Sanitary conveniences

(1) Suitable and sufficient sanitary conveniences must be provided or made available at readily accessible places.

(2) So far as is reasonably practicable, rooms containing sanitary conveniences must be adequately ventilated and lit.

(3) So far as is reasonably practicable, sanitary conveniences and the rooms containing them must be kept in a clean and orderly condition.

(4) Separate rooms containing sanitary conveniences must be provided for men and women, except where and so far as each convenience is in a separate room, the door of which is capable of being secured from the inside.

2. Washing facilities

(1) Suitable and sufficient washing facilities, including showers if required by the nature of the work or for health reasons, must so far as is reasonably practicable, be provided or made available at readily accessible places.

(2) Washing facilities must be provided:

(a) in the immediate vicinity of every sanitary convenience, whether or not also provided elsewhere; and

(b) in the vicinity of any changing rooms required by paragraph 4, whether or not provided elsewhere.

(3) Washing facilities must include:

(a) a supply of clean hot and cold, or warm, water (which must be running water so far as is reasonably practicable)

(b) soap or other suitable means of cleaning; and

(c) towels or other suitable means of drying.

(4) Rooms containing washing facilities must be sufficiently ventilated and lit.

(5) Washing facilities and the rooms containing them must be kept in a clean and orderly condition.

(6) Subject to paragraph (7), separate washing facilities must be provided for men and women, except where they are provided in a room the door of which is capable of being secured from inside and the facilities in each room are intended to be used by only one person at a time.

(7) Sub-paragraph (6) does not apply to facilities which are provided for washing hands, forearms and the face only.

3. Drinking water

(1) An adequate supply of wholesome drinking water must be provided or made available at readily accessible and suitable places.

(2) Where necessary for reasons of health and safety, every supply of drinking water must be conspicuously marked by an appropriate sign.

(3) Where a supply of drinking water is provided a sufficient number of suitable cups or other drinking vessels must also be provided, unless the supply of drinking water is in a jet from which persons can drink easily.

4. Changing rooms and lockers

(1) Suitable and sufficient changing rooms must be provided or made available at readily accessible places if a worker:

(a) has to wear special clothing for the purposes of construction work; and

(b) cannot, for reasons of health or propriety, be expected to change elsewhere.

(2) Where necessary for reasons of propriety, there must be separate changing rooms for, or separate use of rooms by, men and women.

(3) Changing rooms must:

(a) be provided with seating; and

(b) include, where necessary, facilities to enable a person to dry any special clothing and any personal clothing or effects.

(4) Suitable and sufficient facilities must, where necessary, be provided or made available at readily accessible places to enable persons to lock away:

(a) any special clothing which is not taken home

(b) their own clothing which is not worn during working hours; and

(c) their personal effects.

5. Facilities for rest

(1) Suitable and sufficient rest rooms or rest areas must be provided or made available at readily accessible places.

(2) Rest rooms and rest areas must:

- (a) be equipped with an adequate number of tables and adequate seating with backs for the number of persons at work likely to use them at any one time
- (b) where necessary, include suitable facilities for any woman at work who is pregnant or who is a nursing mother to rest lying down
- (c) include suitable arrangements to ensure that meals can be prepared and eaten
- (d) include the means for boiling water; and
- (e) be maintained at an appropriate temperature.

04
Health and safety policies

Contents

Supporting information

G: Checklists and forms

GT 700 Toolbox talks

Overview

By law if a company employs five or more people it must have a written health and safety policy. This contains a statement of general policy on health and safety at work and the organisation and arrangements in place for putting that policy into practice.

This chapter explains what the benefits of a policy are, what it should contain and how it should be used.

4.1 Introduction

A general statement of health and safety policy is the way in which a company sets out its intention to manage health and safety. It will vary from one company to another. There is no such thing as a standard health and safety policy, as a company's policy must be clearly and directly related to its own operations.

It is common for companies to obtain policies via the internet or purchase them from third parties. These are generic, rarely reflect the type of work that is carried out and may lead a company into a false sense of security. The content of the organisation and arrangements sections of the policy should be specific to each company. If a generic policy is used it is likely that there will be serious omissions in its content and therefore in the way that health and safety is managed.

Each company's policy must be based upon its own work, management and organisational structure, and staff competencies.

The act of compiling a health and safety policy will focus the employer, or senior member of staff to whom the job is delegated, on the day-to-day management of health and safety issues. This will help them to become aware of shortcomings, duplications of effort and requirements for certain competences, which can then be rectified.

Evidence shows that companies with a well-structured and properly implemented health and safety policy, together with the organisation and arrangements for putting the policy into effect, have much better overall health and safety performance. Clients and pre-tender documentation now regularly require a company not only to have a health and safety policy, but also to demonstrate its implementation from the most senior management level downwards.

Health and Safety Executive (HSE) construction accident statistics show that the causes of accidents are substantially the same as they were 10 and 20 years ago. Falls from height and being struck by plant, vehicles and falling objects are still the main types of accident on site. In addition work-related ill health statistics are alarmingly high (over 4,000 deaths per year) due to lack of awareness and insufficient control measures, but also because symptoms can take years to develop so work-related health issues aren't seen as requiring immediate action. It is through the on-going development of a company's health and safety policy that shortcomings can be identified and procedures put in place to help eliminate common causes of accidents and reverse this unenviable record.

The HSE also states that between 80% and 90% of all accidents (and occupational ill health) could be prevented by the application of proper and effective health and safety management, both within company premises and on site. A comprehensive and accurate health and safety policy is the basis of an effective management system. A small company working on a small site has the same general health and safety responsibilities as a large company on a large site. Being on a small site does not mean that workers are any less likely to fall from height/fragile roofs, breathe in dust, be trapped in collapsed excavations, or be struck by falling material or reversing vehicles. There is no difference in the standard of protection required during a house extension compared to that for a major construction project; what is likely to differ is the complexity of the management system.

Health and safety, and the provision of proper welfare facilities, are crucial to the proper running of any building, construction or civil engineering project. They are not an add-on, an extra or an afterthought, but should be integrated with the normal day-by-day work of project planning, tendering and management.

4.2 Important points

- ☑ The Health and Safety at Work Act 1974 requires every employer to have a policy on how health and safety will be managed within the company.
- ☑ If there are five or more employees, the policy must be written down.
- ☑ The policy must explain how matters of health and safety will be organised within the company and the arrangements that the company has put in place for implementing the policy.
- ☑ The policy should be periodically reviewed to ensure that it is still current, and amended when necessary, with the content and changes made available to all employees.
- ☑ Before letting contracts, main or principal contractors will often make it a contractual requirement to see a written copy of each contractor's health and safety policy so that an assessment of their health and safety competency can be made, even if the contractor has five or fewer employees and there is no legal need to have one.
- ☑ 'Off the shelf' health and safety policies, obtained from third parties, are unlikely to contain sufficient company-specific content.
- ☑ The policy has little value unless it is communicated to employees.

4.3 Effective health and safety management

The health and safety policy is the first action for delivering effective health and safety arrangements. This is based on the plan, do, check, act model, which replaces *Successful health and safety management* (HSG65).

- ☑ **Plan.** To implement your policy, you need to establish and maintain an effective health and safety management system. *(Details on creating an effective policy are detailed later in this chapter – refer to 4.5 Policy content.)*
- ☑ **Do.** Delivery depends on an effective management system to ensure, so far as is reasonably practicable, the health and safety of employees and other people affected by work activities.
- ☑ **Check.** Monitor and report on health and safety arrangements and the performance of the health and safety policy.
- ☑ **Act.** Review health and safety performance to establish the essential health and safety principles, and review whether the systems implemented are effective in managing risk and protecting people.

4.4 Written policy

The Health and Safety at Work Act 1974 requires all companies and employers who employ five or more people to have a written statement of their general health and safety policy. This will include details of the necessary organisation and arrangements for implementing the health and safety policy.

People who may be working on a training scheme, trainees on work experience and some self-employed people count as employees for the purpose of this requirement.

Even if someone is self-employed or employs fewer than five people, the law still requires them to:

- ☑ **have a health and safety policy, even if it is not written down**
- ☑ **manage their work in such a way as to protect the health and safety of themselves, those working for them, and anyone else who may be affected by their work.**

Clients may, in judging a company's health and safety competence, require that company to have a written policy even if fewer than five people are employed. This is a client's prerogative, which may be reinforced by a contractual requirement. Contractors will have to comply if they want the work.

Whether working as a main or principal contractor or as a contractor, companies must be able to demonstrate how they effectively manage health and safety. If the company cannot demonstrate competence in health and safety issues, it may not be invited to tender in the future. It is no longer acceptable to simply state that the company has been in the industry for many years without experiencing an accident.

Generally, all health and safety legislation requires employers to provide their employees with a place of work that is safe and where risks to health are properly controlled. They are also required to ensure that people who are not their employees are not exposed to risks to their safety and health.

There should be a carefully planned and systematic approach to health and safety issues, where all risks have been assessed and the appropriate control measures put into place.

Irrespective of size, a company must have a general statement of health and safety policy in order to demonstrate to a client or to another contractor that it has committed itself to the principles of health, safety and welfare.

A **health and safety policy** is a statement of how a company will, within its overall business, manage health, safety and welfare for the benefit of its employees and all other persons who may be affected by the company's operations.

4.5 Policy content

Section 2(3) of the Health and Safety at Work Act 1974 requires that a safety policy should cover three distinct aspects.

- ☑ **A general statement of the company's health and safety policy** highlighting the intent of the employer to have high standards of health and safety in the company, including what they intend to achieve and how they will achieve it.
- ☑ **The organisation** within the company for the effective maintenance and implementation of the health and safety management system.
- ☑ **The arrangements** for the effective implementation and on-going monitoring of the health and safety management system.

4.5.1 Section 1. The statement of policy

The statement of policy should demonstrate a clear commitment to health and safety from senior management by declaring how the company intends to manage health, safety and welfare matters in relation to employees and other persons. It should specifically state the name of, and be signed by, the person responsible for health and safety, who should be the managing director or another director to whom responsibility has been delegated. The policy should be reviewed as often as appropriate but at least every 12 months and a new copy signed, dated and displayed to demonstrate that it is a live document.

There should be a declaration that the necessary resources will be provided to ensure the health and safety of all employees. Where there is more than one employer on site, then they must co-operate with each other concerning health and safety.

It is usual for the statement of policy to state the importance that the company places upon the health and safety of its employees and what is required of them to achieve the aims of the policy. It should also clearly state that all employees will be informed of the contents of the health and safety policy and that they will be consulted about its application.

An example of a completed health and safety policy is shown in Appendix A.

4.5.2 Section 2. Organisation

The requirements for this part of the document are shown below.

- ☑ Identify those people within the company who have specific health and safety responsibilities, including the person who has ultimate responsibility for health and safety.
- ☑ Outline the methods by which health and safety procedures and other health and safety issues will be communicated.
- ☑ Explain the methods by which the effectiveness of the health and safety management system will be measured, reviewed and updated where necessary.

The section must clearly state who has to do what in terms of health and safety. For example, it might say that the contracts manager will receive information from the site manager about accidents, how the results of investigations into those accidents will be managed, and that the health and safety manager will notify the HSE when necessary. It should also detail how health and safety information is to be discussed with and brought to the attention of employees, especially those with specific duties highlighted within the document.

For a sole trader or very small firm, all health and safety duties are likely to be the responsibility of a single person.

It is important to remember that once this information is written down, if there is a serious accident, it will be used in court either by the HSE or lawyers in a civil claim. This means people need to be aware of their responsibilities and have the competence to carry them out.

4.5.3 Section 3. Arrangements

This part of the health and safety policy should clearly show the specific arrangements that a company has put in place for managing health and safety during its normal work. It should also detail how emergency situations and any other incidents would be handled both from a management and a site perspective. One area for consideration is for companies to indicate how they compile risk assessments, gather information and develop safe systems of work.

The development of the arrangements section is likely to evolve over a period of time and, to an extent, reflect the findings of the company's risk assessments. It should encompass **who** is responsible, as well as **what** they will do and **when** and **how** they will achieve it.

- ☑ Explain how the need for (health and safety) competences and training are established and satisfied and, if necessary, what interim measures will be put in place whilst shortcomings exist.
- ☑ Outline the means by which health and safety consultation with the workforce will be achieved including, as necessary, reference to management and safety representatives and safety committees.
- ☑ Explain the procedures for ensuring that sub-contractors have a satisfactory health and safety management system and exhibit safe working practices on site.
- ☑ List the areas of risk and identify the person who is responsible for managing each risk.

Some of the elements that might need to be addressed are shown below.

Site activities		Administration procedures
▪ Hot works ▪ Production of dust or fumes ▪ Noise and vibration ▪ Work at height ▪ Confined space entry ▪ Protection of the public ▪ Authorisation for the use of plant and equipment ▪ Lone working ▪ Machine guarding ▪ Loading and unloading	▪ Vehicle movements ▪ Manual handling ▪ Use of access equipment ▪ Scaffolding ▪ Use of ladders and stepladders ▪ Mobile elevating work platforms (MEWPs) ▪ Excavations ▪ Hazardous substances ▪ Working in occupied premises	▪ Emergency procedures ▪ First aid ▪ Fire ▪ Means of escape ▪ Accident reporting ▪ Welfare facilities ▪ Employee consultation ▪ Monitoring for the effectiveness of health and safety procedures

The policy for a company (or sole trader) that carries out a particular trade (such as bricklaying or carpentry and joinery) is likely to be simpler than that for a general builder. This is simply because a jobbing builder may be called upon to carry out a wide range of work. An effective way to deal with the health and safety management in these circumstances might be for the jobbing builder to produce a general policy document and then to supplement it with a set of task-specific documents that work at a site level.

Although the majority of work by a small company may be repetitive, the place of work is likely to vary. For example, installing a new toilet system in a new-build house is basically always the same; but to install one in an occupied house while the occupiers are living in the premises gives rise to other potential problems.

This is where so-called generic arrangements need to be site specific. The major weakness of this situation will become apparent if office-based staff develop and issue arrangements that do not reflect actual site conditions.

The arrangements section of the policy must demonstrate clearly how the company plans to carry out its work and should identify all the specific site risks associated with them.

Employers are legally required to give their employees all the information, instruction, training and supervision necessary to ensure their health and safety.

The arrangements section of the policy should also cover the situation where a manager is unable to visit a possible work site whilst tendering or preparing a quotation for a job, but instead sends an estimator. In this case the estimator must be trained to assess the health and safety risks of the work, and record the work to be done and the risk control measures necessary.

These notes should indicate all possible hazards, working height, obstructions, and plant and equipment required. Detailed risk assessments can then be carried out and the associated method statements developed. This will allow for employees to be properly instructed on or informed about the work that they are to do.

However, on small works of short duration or emergency repairs, detailed pre-planning may not be possible. Employees may be sent to a client's premises or a customer's house at very short notice. This type of work may create a number of problems for employees, including the need for a short notice or on-site risk assessment, and the arrangements section of the company health and safety policy must cater for this type of eventuality.

Managing health and safety on a large site offers certain challenges, but it is normally far easier than dealing with a large number of minor works. This is purely down to the level of supervision and control that can be put in place.

There is a certain irony that typically it is the smallest and probably least resourced organisations that have the biggest challenges in terms of developing management systems.

4.6 Updating safety policies

The law requires that employers revise their safety policies as often as may be appropriate. This means they should be updated in the light of any new legislation, HSE or industry guidance, British or European Standards, together with taking into account the actual experience in operating with the policy.

Changes in the type of work carried out, changes in staff and as a result of any accidents or incidents will also give rise to the need for a review of the policy. In addition, the policy should be regularly reviewed to ensure that it stays meaningful and relevant to the company's overall operations.

Good practice is for an annual review of the policy, with the policy being re-signed, dated and any changes communicated. Even if there are no required changes, it should still be re-signed and dated in order for the company to demonstrate a review has taken place. This is important for companies that have to provide copies of their policy for a third-party assessment scheme or to prospective clients.

4.7 Communication

Employers are legally required to bring their health and safety policy, and any subsequent revisions to it, to the notice of all employees. CDM emphasises the need for consultation and engagement with the workers. Communicating the health and safety policy is a good way of doing this.

As can be seen from the 'back to the shop floor' programmes on television, often the reality of workplace conditions and the practices that have developed escape the notice of senior management. This may be because pressures, techniques, environments and expectations change over a period of time.

The only way to find out if the requirements of the policy are realistic and workable is to talk to the people who have to comply with them in the workplace.

Under the Information and Consultation of Employees Regulations, employers with more than 50 staff are required to provide information and consultation agreements where over 10% of staff formally request it.

This legislation was not made under the Health and Safety at Work Act 1974 and is not therefore enforceable by the HSE but by an industrial court. However, it provides a further opportunity to consult staff over a range of issues, including health and safety under the Health and Safety (Consultation with Employees) Regulations and the Safety Representatives and Safety Committees Regulations.

4.8 Advice on preparation

4.8.1 Construction (Design and Management) Regulations

The client is responsible for making suitable arrangements for managing a project that enables duty holders to ensure construction work is carried out in a way that secures health, safety and welfare.

Those responsible for making appointments under the regulations must take reasonable steps to satisfy themselves that those bidding for the work have the necessary skills, knowledge, training and experience and, where they are an organisation, the organisational capability, to carry out the work in a way that secures health and safety. Part of the approval process must be a review and critical examination of the duty holder's health and safety policy.

It could be a good idea for organisations and individuals bidding for work to compile a competence pack to show how their policies, organisation and arrangements meet the stipulated core criteria for managing health and safety.

However, for low risk, low value jobs, simply providing a copy of the health and safety policy statement and the index page for the arrangements might be deemed sufficient. Obviously, it is much easier to send the whole document if all parts are available electronically.

Appendix A contains a suggested layout of a health and safety policy for a medium-sized company carrying out small building works. Not all of it will be relevant to some companies and, conversely, it may not contain specific content that some companies require.

- ☑ For most companies, the general statement of health and safety policy should fit onto one side of A4 paper.
- ☑ The organisation and arrangements sections will be longer depending on the size of the company and the type of work that is carried out.
- ☑ Overall, the final document should be a clear indication to clients, employees and other interested parties (such as the HSE) that the company is honestly, openly and totally committed to the proper and effective management of all aspects of health, safety and welfare.

For an example of a health and safety policy template refer to Section G: *Checklists and forms.*

For guidance on the preparation of health and safety policy documents refer to the HSE website.

4.9 The business case

In addition to the legal considerations (for example, compliance with the law) there are very strong economic and social drivers for a robust health and safety policy and its proper implementation.

The economic argument is that if there are fewer accidents on site and no occupational ill health, more employees will be at work rather than off sick. This means improved business continuity with a greater prospect of completing projects on time, to budget and to the satisfaction of the client.

The social argument is similar. Clients and customers are far more likely to place business with a company who they see is behaving with integrity, and taking proper care of the health, safety and welfare of their employees and others who might be affected by the work of the company.

Clients, in particular Local Authority clients, assessing the competence of small companies that are seeking approval for entry onto approved lists will be looking for evidence of effective health and safety management. Some Local Authorities use a standard questionnaire, which asks companies to provide comprehensive details on the following.

- ☑ The competent person who provides health and safety advice.
- ☑ Its general policy on health and safety, its organisation and arrangements for implementing the policy.
- ☑ Training provision and training providers.
- ☑ Accident statistics, copies of enforcement notices and details of any prosecution (these do not mean the automatic exclusion of the company).
- ☑ Arrangements for distributing new health and safety information.
- ☑ Examples of risk assessments.
- ☑ Arrangements for liaison with clients.
- ☑ Management arrangements (such as audits and inspection reports).
- ☑ Health surveillance (where applicable).
- ☑ Arrangements for assessing contractors.
- ☑ Where applicable, the ability to undertake roles under the Construction (Design and Management) Regulations.

A well-structured health and safety policy will provide a great deal of this information, and any additional information needed can easily be incorporated as an annexe to the policy.

If a company is successful in gaining entry onto an approved list for one Local Authority, it will then be much easier to seek similar approval from other authorities.

4.10 Third-party contractor assessment

Being able to prove your health and safety competence in the construction industry is a crucial element to securing contracts. Clients will always seek highly competent principal contractors who then, in turn, will look for the same in the sub-contractors that they employ.

The Construction (Design and Management) Regulations state that both contractors and sub-contractors must be able to demonstrate Stage 1 competence, which can be approved through an independent assessment scheme.

Assessing health and safety competence can be a complicated and time consuming process. There are two levels that need to be considered.

Stage 1 – The primary level. This is the ability of an organisation to prove that their arrangements for managing health and safety are sufficient to allow them to carry out work safely and without risk to the health of their workers.

Stage 2 – The second level assesses competence in relation to experience and the needs of the particular job. It looks at an individual's track record of working on similar types of project to those being tendered for.

Several schemes have been developed to help clients and contractors alike to meet their obligation to only appoint competent contractors.

The schemes are a pre-qualification assessment designed around the requirements of CDM. Competence is assessed against the criteria set out in Stage 1 including, amongst others, the requirements for contractors to have a health and safety policy, access to competent health and safety advice and to ensure employees are appropriately trained.

By satisfying the scheme assessment, the contractor is able to demonstrate Stage 1 competence to future employers, avoiding the need to repeat the process for every client or contractor worked for. This also helps those buying services from contractors, as they need only worry about Stage 2 type assessments (for example, matching the experience of the contractor to the work being undertaken).

4.10.1 Safety schemes in procurement

In April 2007, an initial meeting was held at the Health and Safety Executive's headquarters, which included representatives from the **Contractors' Health and Safety Assessment Scheme (CHAS), Constructionline, Exor,** and the **National House-building Council (NHBC)** to discuss the potential for the Safety Schemes in Procurement (SSIP) forum.

Following further regular meetings over the next two years, SSIP forum founder members agreed and signed up to achieve the following.

- ☑ Act as an umbrella organisation to facilitate mutual recognition between health and safety pre-qualification schemes wherever it is practicable to do so.
- ☑ Actively advise and influence clients about acceptable interpretation and appropriateness of health and safety competence standards in UK schemes.
- ☑ Embrace the core guidance on skills, knowledge, training and experience of the Construction (Design and Management) Regulations.

SSIP forum members are committed to avoiding duplication within pre-qualification. If contractors have already been assessed by another SSIP member they can apply for registration for another SSIP recognised scheme, usually by downloading and completing the 'Deem to satisfy' application form.

More information about the scheme can be found on the SSIP website.

4.10.2 Contractors' Health and Safety Assessment Scheme

The Contractors' Health and Safety Assessment Scheme (CHAS) is a pre-qualification scheme, widely used to identify companies that have demonstrated, through the CHAS assessment process, that they have a robust approach to health and safety management.

CHAS assesses applicants in the following areas.

- ☑ Health and safety policy statements.
- ☑ The health and safety arrangements of their organisation.
- ☑ Their specific health and safety arrangements to a standard acceptable to buyers and others.

The scheme is a private limited company owned by the London Borough of Merton and concentrates on what it refers to as fundamental health and safety management and compliance issues related to the type of work the applicant has suggested they do.

More information about the scheme can be found on the CHAS website.

4.10.3 Constructionline

Constructionline is the Government's national register and is the UK's largest register for pre-qualified contractors and consultants. It is a public-private partnership between Capita and the Department for Business Innovation and Skills. Like CHAS, Constructionline provides a pre-qualification tool for use in financial standing, technical references and other areas. The CHAS management group supports the principles of a single register and so works jointly with Constructionline.

CHAS and Constructionline have formed a mutual working agreement. This sets out how they will work together to provide an improved service for the industry's clients. CHAS and Constructionline are independent bodies but their databases are linked. It is therefore possible that not having an acceptable health and safety policy could be detrimental to company assessment by Constructionline.

More information about the scheme can be found on the Constructionline website.

4.10.4 Safecontractor

Safecontractor is a health and safety assessment scheme with more than 220 major clients and over 22,000 contractor members.

Registered members with the Safecontractor scheme include clients and contractors from a wide range of professional disciplines working within a number of industry sectors. The Safecontractor scheme is now used by many large organisations as a way of obtaining competent contractors.

More information about the scheme can be found on the Safecontractor website.

4.10.5 Safemark

Safemark is the health and safety competence assessment scheme of NHBC. It's the only such scheme designed by house-building specialists for house builders. It is recognised by Safety Schemes in Procurement (SSIP).

More information about the scheme can be found on the NHBC website.

Appendix A – Example health and safety policy

HSE **Example health and safety policy** Health and Safety Executive

Example policy for an alarm installation company

Setting the scene

Daly Response Alarm Systems supply and install intruder alarms to residential and business premises. Manager and founder John Daly employs a total of 22 staff, consisting of an assistant manager, a receptionist, three customer service support advisers, four sales representatives, two accounts assistants, a head engineer and ten site engineers.

The office is open Monday to Friday 9.00-5.30 and Saturday morning 9.00-12.00 and cleaning is shared by the office-based staff, who have a rota.

John Daly prepared his own health and safety policy statement, using the combined template available on the HSE website at www.hse.gov.uk/risk/risk-assessment-and-policy-template.doc
He genuinely cares for his staff and wants to portray this in his health and safety policy.

John downloaded the template and referred to the example policy statement and other guidance available on the HSE website at www.hse.gov.uk/risk. This helped him to think about the things that should be documented and built into his own health and safety policy, such as remote working, personal protective equipment, staff consultation and training etc. He decided that he and his assistant manager would be the most competent (experienced and capable) people to take responsibility for health and safety issues.

John presented the policy statement at the staff meeting and decided to review and update the document every year or straightaway if there are any major changes in the workplace.

A
04

Employers with less than five employees don't have to write down their health and safety policy.
For further information and to view our example risk assessments, see www.hse.gov.uk/risk.
Example health and safety policy published by the Health and Safety Executive 08/14

HSE **Example health and safety policy** Health and Safety Executive

This is the statement of general policy and arrangements for:	**Daly Response Alarm Systems**
John Daly – Manager	**has overall and final responsibility for health and safety**
Paul Phillips – Assistant Manager	**has day-to-day responsibility for ensuring this policy is put into practice**

Statement of general policy	Responsibility of: Name/Title	Action/Arrangements (What are you going to do?)
Prevent accidents and cases of work-related ill health by managing the health and safety risks in the workplace	John Daly Manager	Relevant risk assessments completed and actions arising out of those assessments implemented. (Risk assessments reviewed when working habits or conditions change.)
Provide clear instructions and information, and adequate training, to ensure employees are competent to do their work	Paul Phillips Assistant Manager	Staff and subcontractors given necessary health and safety induction and provided with appropriate training (including working at height, asbestos awareness and electrical safety) and personal protective equipment. We will ensure that suitable arrangements are in place to cover employees engaged in work remote from the main company site.
Engage and consult with employees on day-to-day health and safety conditions	John Daly (Manager) Paul Phillips (Assistant Manager) All staff	Staff routinely consulted on health and safety matters as they arise but also formally consulted at regular health and safety performance review meetings or sooner if required.
Implement emergency procedures – evacuation in case of fire or other significant incident. You can find help with your fire risk assessment at: https://www.gov.uk/workplace-fire-safety-your-responsibilities	John Daly Manager	Escape routes well signed and kept clear at all times. Evacuation plans are tested from time to time and updated as necessary.
Maintain safe and healthy working conditions, provide and maintain plant, equipment and machinery, and ensure safe storage/use of substances	Paul Phillips Assistant Manager	Toilets, washing facilities and drinking water provided. System in place for routine inspections and testing of equipment and machinery and for ensuring that action is promptly taken to address any defects.

Signed: * (Employer)	*J Daly*	Date:	*28th August 2014*

You should review your policy if you think it might no longer be valid, eg if circumstances change. If you have fewer than five employees, you don't have to write down your policy.

Health and safety law poster is displayed at (location)	Reception
First-aid box is located:	Staff room
Accident book is located:	Reception

Accidents and ill health at work reported under RIDDOR (Reporting of Injuries, Diseases and Dangerous Occurrences Regulations) http://www.hse.gov.uk/riddor
To get an interactive version of this template go to http://www.hse.gov.uk/risk/risk-assessment-and-policy-template.doc
Combined risk assessment and policy template published by the Health and Safety Executive 08/14

05

Risk assessments and method statements

Contents

Supporting information

G: Checklists and forms

GT 700 Toolbox talks

Overview

The assessment of risk is the fundamental principle behind the drive for a reduction of workplace accidents and work-related ill health.

Risk assessments and method statements need to be suitable and proportionate to the risks, specific to the site and task, and fully understood and appreciated by the workforce.

Assessing risk is not a difficult process, but sadly many companies rely on folders full of generic risk assessments and method statements that bear little resemblance to how their workforce actually carry out the work.

5.1 Introduction

The principle of risk assessment is a fundamental cornerstone of the management of health and safety in the workplace. Legislation places a legal duty on employers to assess the risks, to the health and safety of their employees and others, that arise out of their work.

There is also a requirement in other sets of regulations for employers to carry out risk assessments in relation to specific threats to health or safety in the workplace, such as those shown below.

- ☑ The use of hazardous substances.
- ☑ Noise in the workplace.
- ☑ Manual handling.
- ☑ The presence of asbestos.
- ☑ Work at height.
- ☑ Work with vibrating tools and equipment.

However, this does not put an obligation on employers to carry out two risk assessments for the same hazard. If the general risk assessment covers the specified hazards, that risk assessment alone will be sufficient.

Risk assessment

There is no legal definition of a risk assessment but in practice it can be said to be a careful and structured examination of a work activity so as to identify:

- ☑ what could cause harm (the hazards) to people (employees or others)
- ☑ how, by the use of appropriate control measures, the risks (the chance that the hazard will cause harm) arising from the hazards may be eliminated or controlled.

The amount of effort that needs to be put into carrying out a risk assessment should be appropriate and proportional to the nature of the hazard and the perceived level of risk.

It is essential that all high risks are assessed and controlled first, before looking at the medium risks. Only look at the low risks once all high and medium risks have been either eliminated or adequately controlled.

Simple work activities with few hazards, which present a low risk, should need only simple assessments.

If a risk assessment is to be effective, it is essential that the person who carries it out is familiar with all aspects of the task being assessed.

Risk assessments do not necessarily need to be carried out by a health and safety professional. When the task being assessed is often repeated or is otherwise familiar, simple or routine, managers and supervisors will often be sufficiently knowledgeable and competent to carry out a risk assessment.

However, where a task presents complex, unusual or technical issues it may be necessary to seek the advice of a competent person, or to seek advice from other sources, such as the Health and Safety Executive (HSE) or the health and safety helpline of a relevant trade organisation.

5.2 Important points

- The assessment of risk is the fundamental principle behind the drive for a reduction of workplace accidents and work-related ill health.
- Employers with five or more employees are required by law to record the significant findings of their risk assessments.
- Main (or principal) contractors may wish to see written risk assessments from any contractor they intend to employ, regardless of the number of employees.
- Risk assessments must consider the potential risks to the health and/or safety of anyone who may be adversely affected, which may include employees, the employees of other contractors, site visitors, members of the public, and so on.
- Carrying out risk assessments need not be difficult or unduly time-consuming; the effort should be proportionate to the degree of perceived risk.
- There is no official content or way of structuring a risk assessment; it is for each employer to decide what works best for their undertaking.
- It is vital that written risk assessments and method statements are presented in an easy to understand format for those that are actually doing the work.
- Method statements are a way of integrating the information gained during the risk assessment process into a structured sequence of work for completing a job.

5.3 Terms used in risk assessment

Anyone carrying out risk assessments must be familiar with the meaning of the following terms that are used in process.

- **Hazard:** anything that has the potential to cause harm (ill health, injury or damage).
- **Risk:** the likelihood of an event occurring from a hazard.
- **Likelihood:** the chance that an accident will occur (certain, likely, possible, unlikely or rare).
- **Severity:** the severity (consequences) of any incident that arises.
- **Danger:** a person is in danger when they are exposed to a risk.
- **Accident:** an event that results in damage, injury or ill health.
- **Near miss:** (including dangerous occurrence) an event that, while not causing harm, has the potential to cause injury or ill health.
- **Competence:** having practical and theoretical knowledge, training and actual experience of the work involved.

e.g. **Severity**

- At one extreme, someone who is buried in a collapsed excavation could be killed, whereas, at the other end of the scale, the consequences of someone not using a hand tool correctly might only be grazed skin or a cut.
- When assessing risk to health, severity can be misunderstood or underestimated. Someone breathing in silica dust for a day or two will not seemingly be harmed, but continual exposure over many months or years could lead to a fatal lung disease.

5.4 Legislative requirements

5.4.1 Principles of risk assessment

All recent health and safety legislation is structured around a goal-setting or risk-based approach to the management of health and safety in the workplace.

Employers are required to establish systems that identify hazards, assess the associated risks, develop and implement suitable control measures, and monitor the adequacy and effectiveness of such risk control systems.

Employers' responsibilities are shown below.

- **Identify the hazards** (things with the potential to cause harm) that arise out of the work activity being assessed.
- **Assess the risks** to the health and safety of any person(s) who is likely to be affected by the hazards.
- **Identify the individuals** or groups of people who are at risk.
- **Eliminate the hazards** (where possible) thereby removing the risk of injury.
- **Identify and implement** appropriate measures to control the remaining risks.
- **Effectively monitor and review** the control measures established for the work activity and amend them if they are no longer valid or become ineffective.

5.4.2 Management of Health and Safety at Work Regulations

These regulations require employers to carry out a suitable and sufficient assessment of the risks to health and safety for all work carried out.

When carrying out risk assessments, employers must consider not only the wellbeing of their own employees, but also anyone else who may be affected by that work activity.

This includes, but is not restricted to the following.

- The employees of other contractors or the self-employed.
- Site visitors (such as delivery drivers).
- Members of the public, including children.
- The client, customers or other occupiers of the property.

Particular provision is made in the regulations for the protection of young persons in the workplace.

Although not mentioned in the regulations, it is implicit that any risk assessment must, where appropriate, take into account the requirements of anyone on site who may suffer from a disability (for example, someone who is partially or totally deaf).

The duty to undertake risk assessments is placed on all employers irrespective of the number of persons they employ but, where five or more persons are employed, the significant findings of the assessment must be recorded (either in writing or electronically). However, clients may, if they choose, require contractors to produce recorded risk assessments even when fewer than five persons are employed by them. The self-employed have a similar duty to undertake risk assessments for the work that they do, to identify the risks to the health and safety of both themselves and others who may be affected by the work that they carry out.

Once the risk assessment has been carried out, employers must then implement the control measures that are necessary to protect those at risk. It is then very important to ensure that the significant findings of the risk assessment are made known to all persons who are likely to be involved in the work or affected by it.

In order to understand the principles of risk assessment, it is necessary to first understand the meaning of the terms used, as defined by the HSE in its publication *Five steps to risk assessment*.

A **hazard** is anything with the **potential** to cause harm. Examples are electricity, noise, vibration, chemicals, asbestos, working at height, working over water, excavations, confined spaces, manual handling, falling materials, and the use of tools, plant and vehicles.

A **risk** is the **likelihood** that the **hazard** will actually cause harm.

e.g. Risks of working at height

If working from a ladder the likelihood of the person falling (the hazard) could be regarded as high when compared with doing the same job from a scaffold platform fitted with guard-rails. A control measure (the scaffold) has been introduced and so the likelihood of the hazard occurring is significantly reduced.

The regulations require that all risk assessments are **suitable** and **sufficient**. For a risk assessment to comply with this requirement it must achieve the following.

- Establish the risks arising from the work activity.
- Be appropriate, given the nature of the work, such that it remains valid for a reasonable period of time.
- Be proportionate to the level of risk and the nature of the work.
- Identify and prioritise the control measures required to protect the health and safety of the employees and others who may be affected.

Furthermore, to be suitable and sufficient each risk assessment must take account of any factors that could change during the course of the job, thereby introducing additional hazards or increasing the level of risk arising from existing hazards. Examples of this are variable labour levels, being asked at short notice to do something a different way to accommodate others and work or hired equipment having to be returned if the job overruns.

The law does not expect you to eliminate all risk, but you are required to protect people as far as is reasonably practicable.

5.4.3 Young persons and children

Regulation 19 of the Management of Health and Safety at Work Regulations contain specific provisions in respect of the health and safety of children and young persons. Employers are required to specifically assess and review the risks to the health and safety of children and young persons on construction sites due to their lack of maturity, experience, or knowledge of potential risks.

Young persons and children

- A ***young person*** is anyone under the age of 18.
- A ***child*** is anyone who has not yet reached the official minimum school leaving age. Pupils reach the minimum school leaving age in the school year in which they turn 16.

Children under 13 years cannot be employed at all. At the age of 13 they can work part time and can start full time work (40 hours a week) when they reach the minimum school leaving age.

If someone starts work at the age of 16 they are paid through PAYE. At the age of 18 adult employment rights and rules apply.

Children between 13 and the minimum school leaving age may, in accordance with local by-laws, with the permission of the Local Authority and after significant risks have been explained to the parents or carers, attend a construction site for site visits and organised work experience. If a child is employed on work experience the employers' liability insurance policy will cover the work placement, as long as the insurer is a member of the Association of British Insurers or Lloyds.

Furthermore, there will be occasions when 14 to 16-year-old children are on site under the Young Apprentice Training Scheme. If children will be doing or observing work on a construction site the employer must consider the risk involved and they must be satisfied that the instruction, training and supervisory arrangements have been properly thought through and work in practice.

Where children are employed either for work experience or work in offices then the employer must, before commencing the employment of the child, provide that child's parents or guardians with details of any risk assessment that has been carried out. This information must contain details of any risk and a description of any preventative or protective measures, whether the risk arises from the employer's own activity or the work of others at the workplace.

Before a young person or child is employed, the employer must ensure that any risk assessments pertaining to the job take account of the following factors in relation to the young person.

- ☑ Their inexperience.
- ☑ Their immaturity and lack of awareness of risks.
- ☑ The tools and equipment that they may have to use as part of their training.
- ☑ The layout of the workplace and the environment in which they may have to work.
- ☑ Any hazardous substances with which they may come into contact.
- ☑ Exposure to physical, chemical or biological hazards.
- ☑ The organisation of work and work processes.
- ☑ The extent of health and safety training that is to be provided.

Careful consideration must be given to the way in which information is conveyed to young persons to ensure that it is fully and readily understood.

Employers are further required to consider the special nature of young persons due to their lack of experience, knowledge of risks and the fact that they are not fully mature. To that end, young people must not be employed in any of the following work.

- ☑ That which they cannot physically or psychologically cope with.
- ☑ That which exposes them to a range of hazardous substances, including any carcinogen, toxic substance or radiation.
- ☑ Where they might not recognise the risk of accidents due to their inexperience or lack of training.
- ☑ Where their health would be at risk from excessive cold, heat, noise or vibration.

The prohibition above does not apply when a young person is undergoing recognised training, or when they are being properly supervised by a competent person, or when any risks identified in a risk assessment have been reduced to the lowest level that is reasonably practicable.

For the training provision to apply, the training must be necessary within a trade or occupation, and be part of an identified unit of NVQ, SVQ or other similar work-related qualification.

www.

For further information on employing young persons and children refer to the HSE website.

5.4.4 Expectant and nursing mothers

In accordance with Regulations 16 to 18 special consideration must be given within risk assessments to any employee who is pregnant, has given birth within the past six months or who is breastfeeding, where the nature of the work would put her or her unborn child at risk.

The assessment may identify the need to temporarily alter the work environment, work pattern, work activity or working hours and provide additional facilities or support. If this is not possible the employee should be offered suitable alternative work (at the same rate of pay). If this is not available or feasible then the employee will need to be suspended from work on paid leave for as long as necessary in order to protect their child's health and safety.

Any employee who is pregnant, has given birth within the past six months or who is breastfeeding must notify her employer in writing of her condition within a reasonable length of time.

For an expectant mothers' risk assessment refer to Section G: *Checklists and forms.*

For further information refer to *Guidance for new and expectant mothers who work,* available from the HSE website, and *What you need to know as an employer,* available from the Department for Business Innovation and Skills website.

5.5 Understanding control hierarchy

Preventative and **protective** (control measures) must be taken to address the hazards and to eliminate or reduce the risks to an acceptable level.

Using a remote controlled trench compactor eliminated the need for a person to be in the excavation

These measures must be based upon the general principles of prevention.

- Avoiding risks where possible.
- Evaluating risks that cannot be avoided.
- Combating risks at source.
- Adapting the work of an individual, especially regarding the:
  - design of the workplace
  - choice of work equipment
  - choice of working and production methods.
- Adapting to technical progress.
- Replacing the dangerous with the safe or less dangerous.
- Developing a coherent prevention policy that covers:
  - technology
  - organisation of work
  - working conditions
  - social relationships.
- Giving collective measures priority over measures that protect the individual.
- Giving appropriate instructions to employees.

5.6 Five steps to risk assessment

The HSE previously issued guidance, known as the five steps to risk assessment, which has now been replaced. However, new guidance still suggests that the following steps should be covered.

- Step 1. Identify the hazards.
- Step 2. Think about who might be harmed.
- Step 3. Evaluate the risks.
- Step 4. Record your significant findings.
- Step 5. Review your risk assessment.

The new guidance, in addition to the five steps, makes it clear that only significant findings need to be recorded and greater emphasis should be placed on the importance of controlling the risks.

5.6.1 Step 1. Identify the hazards

Some typical examples of hazards found on construction sites are shown below.

- An untidy site with lots of slipping and tripping hazards.
- The use of equipment with rotating blades (such as disc cutters).
- The use of power tools creating dust.
- The risk of fire from spark-emitting tools (such as angle grinders).
- Work at height with the potential for falls (for example, roofing work).
- Manual handling work or working in cramped conditions.
- The operation of construction plant near to people on foot.
- The presence of contaminated ground.
- The use of chemicals, solvents, paints, and so on.

5.6.2 Step 2. Think about who might be harmed

Having established the hazards associated with the job you will have to identify the individuals or groups of people who are at risk, such as those shown below.

- Yourself.
- Other employees (particularly anyone young and inexperienced).
- Employees who need special consideration (for example, someone who is deaf or who is not fluent in English).
- Employees who are pregnant, or nursing mothers.
- Employees of other contractors.
- Visitors (such as delivery drivers, maintenance staff and clients).
- Members of the public or trespassers (particularly children).
- Anyone else who might be affected by your work (for example, neighbouring businesses).

5.6.3 Evaluate the risks

Having identified the hazards, now consider what risk-control measures are necessary to keep the people who have been identified as being at risk from harm.

Even when precautions have been put in place there will usually be a remaining (residual) risk. You will have to exercise your judgement as to whether, in your opinion, the residual risk is high, medium or low. This part of the assessment is a loop.

If after identifying risk control measures you think that the level of residual risk is still too high, it will be necessary to introduce further control measures, again evaluate the level of residual risk and continue the process until it is considered to be acceptable.

It is a case of you asking yourself 'What have I done to control the risks and what more do I need to do?'

Considerations when establishing controls

When establishing appropriate control measures, consideration should be given to the following techniques.

- **Combat risks at source** – for example, use a safer method (such as using a block splitter instead of a petrol cut-off saw).
- **Take advantage of technical progress** and adopt new, safer methods of working. For example, use a modern trestle system, complete with guard-rails and toe-boards, rather than scaffold boards supported on improvised hop ups.
- **Replace the dangerous with the non-dangerous or less dangerous** – for example, prohibit the use of all 230 V power tools, allowing only 110 V or battery-powered tools.
- **Adopt measures that protect the greatest number of individuals** – for example, safety nets protect everyone working above them, whereas a safety harness only protects the wearer.
- **Give appropriate information**, instructions and training to employees and others – assess the need for training.
- **Provide PPE – always the very last resort.**

5.6.4 Step 4. Record your significant findings

Health and safety law requires that all employers carry out risk assessments for their work, although legally only employers with five or more employees need record the significant findings of their risk assessments.

However, in practice, many of the larger contractors will not accept any sub-contractor on site, even those with fewer than five employees, if they do not have written risk assessments. Risk assessments may be recorded electronically providing that they may be easily retrieved for scrutiny if required.

In the interests of clarity, risk assessments may identify where relevant supporting information can be found (such as the company health and safety policy), rather than including masses of information in the risk assessment itself. However, if this approach is taken, the supporting documents may also have to be supplied to whoever wishes to see the risk assessment.

The law does not specify how a risk assessment should be laid out although two common conventions have evolved over time.

- **Quantitive risk assessment** – outlines the hazards present and the risk control measures necessary, and in which residual risk is given a numerical score or categorised as high, medium or low to enable corrective actions to be prioritised.
- **Qualitative risk assessment** – in which the process is the same. No attempt is made to quantify the level of residual risk.

Examples of both types of risk assessment are included later in this chapter *(refer to 5.7)*.

Irrespective of how a risk assessment is laid out, it is considered good practice for it to identify the following.

- Person who will manage the residual risks.
- Date(s) by which any essential actions must be taken, in the interests of health or safety.
- Review date.

5.6.5 Step 5. Review the risk assessment

Risk assessments should be reviewed from time to time to ensure the control measures are still appropriate and effective. If there is a change to any aspect of the way the job has to be carried out that might affect health and safety (for example having to use a different item of equipment part way through the job, the arrival of a new operative who is inexperienced, unexpected deteriorating weather or the late arrival of materials) the assessment must be reviewed and the risks re-evaluated.

www. **The HSE has produced *A brief guide to controlling risks in the workplace.***

5.7 Types of risk assessment

The risk of something going wrong is considered in terms of probability (likelihood) and consequences (seriousness).

5.7.1 Generic risk assessments

- ☑ A generic risk assessment is an assessment that may be used more than once because the job to which it relates is being repeated and it can be guaranteed that the hazards and level of risk are the same on each occasion that the job is carried out.
- ☑ When an employer intends to rely on a generic risk assessment, great care must be taken to ensure that there are no factors that could introduce additional hazards or increase the level of risk.
- ☑ In many cases, generic risk assessments are not acceptable within the construction industry because each site is different and conditions change as construction work progresses.

A
05

www. **The HSE report *Good practice and pitfalls in risk assessment* can be found on its website.**

5.7.2 HSE risk assessments

The HSE has produced a simple template that does not use ratings, but instead uses the headings listed below. Some prefer this method as it follows logical risk assessment steps. It can also be easier for the workforce to understand.

What are the hazards?	Who might be harmed and how?	What are you already doing?	Do you need to do anything else to control the risk?	Action by who?	Action by when?	Done

The HSE has made this template available in Word format and produced a series of example risk assessments, which can be found on its website.

The HSE's example risk assessment for a plastering company can be found in Appendix A.

5.7.3 Qualitative assessments

The **probability** of a hazard actually causing harm or an accident is rated as being high, medium or low in accordance with the following.

- ☑ **High:** it will happen regularly, or it could be a usual or a common occurrence.
- ☑ **Medium:** it is less regular, but is still recognised as being likely to happen.
- ☑ **Low:** it has not happened for a long time, is known to be infrequent and is not likely to happen.

The **consequences** of the event, should it happen, can then be categorised as follows.

- ☑ **High:** the result could be a fatal accident or multiple injuries/major property damage/substantial pollution or environmental impact.
- ☑ **Medium:** it would probably cause serious injuries (or persons would be off work for over seven days due to their injuries), substantial property damage or there may be some pollution.
- ☑ **Low:** there would be minor injuries to persons or some slight damage to property.

Probability and consequences can then be shown on a matrix as follows.

Probability	High			
	Medium			
	Low			
		Low	Medium	High
		Consequences		

Probability and consequences can then be assessed and the highest outcome of the two entered in the matrix as follows.

Probability	High	High	High	High
	Medium	Medium	Medium	High
	Low	Low	Medium	High
		Low	Medium	High
		Consequences		

- ☑ A combined risk of **high** should be totally unacceptable and the work should not be undertaken until the risk has been reduced.
- ☑ When there is a combined risk of **medium**, action must be taken and work stopped if necessary to reduce the risk level.
- ☑ If the combined risk is **low**, start the work as long as everything reasonably practicable has been done in order to reduce the risk, and review the assessment at regular intervals.

Using this information, decisions can now be made on whether an activity is safe to continue, or whether control measures are necessary, either to completely change the way that the job is done or measures put in place so as to bring the risks down to an acceptable level. In the ideal situation, both probability and consequences should be **low**.

5.7.4 Quantitative assessments

The principle is the same as for qualitative assessments, but numerical scores rather than a grade are assigned to probability and consequences. The probability or likelihood of the event is rated on a scale of one to five, as shown below.

5 **Certain** to happen.

4 **Very likely** to happen, and would not be at all unusual.

3 **Likely** to happen, and would not be totally unexpected.

2 **Unlikely** to happen, but not by any means impossible.

1 **Very unlikely** to happen.

The consequences or the severity of the event, should it happen, are also then rated on a scale of one to five, as shown below.

1 No injury, ill health or damage. It would be a near miss.

2 Minor injury or minor ill health complaint, no time lost. Minor property damage or minor environmental incident.

3 Lost time injury, up to and including reportable injury to the HSE with over seven days' time lost, but not a specified injury. Some risk of immediate or long-term health issues. Significant property damage or local environmental damage.

4 Specified injury, long-term absence or significant risk that could lead to immediate or long-term health illness, including reportable disease. Substantial property damage, serious environmental impact.

5 Fatal accident or multiple specified injuries. Catastrophic event or environmental disaster. Public or others could be involved as well.

A matrix can then be constructed using these numbers, as follows:

Probability	5					
	4					
	3					
	2					
	1					
		1	2	3	4	5
		Consequences				

A
05

All possible resulting numbers are calculated by multiplying all the probability figures by all the consequence figures. These are included in the matrix, as shown below. This means that once a risk assessment has been made on a particular activity, and the probability factor is multiplied by the consequence factor, the number produced indicates where the assessment places the risk associated with the activity on the matrix.

Probability	5	5	10	15	20	25
	4	4	8	12	16	20
	3	3	6	9	12	15
	2	2	4	6	8	10
	1	1	2	3	4	5
		1	2	3	4	5
		Consequences				

Clearly, the higher the resulting number the less acceptable the level of risk. The matrix shows where actions need to be taken to reduce either the probability or the consequences in order to reduce the risks to an acceptable level.

Employers themselves can use these numbers to set in-house criteria, if desired, along the following lines, and as indicated by the shaded areas in the above matrix.

Risk rating	Colour	Risk description
Above 15	(red)	Totally unacceptable and the work will not be undertaken until the risk has been significantly reduced.
Between 9 and 14	(amber)	Immediate action must be taken, including a stoppage of work, if necessary, to reduce the risk level to acceptable.
Between 5 and 8	(green)	Acceptable, provided that everything reasonably practicable has been done to reduce the risk.
4 or less		Acceptable, provided that the assessment is reviewed at regular intervals and further reduced if possible.

It is stressed that it is for individual companies or managers to decide where the boundaries between what is and what is not acceptable lie, and the numerical score at which certain actions should be taken. The above matrix is only an indication of what can be done.

If either the qualitative or quantitative methods are used in conjunction with a simple form, then the employer will have a straightforward, basic risk assessment procedure.

5.8 Risk assessment in practice

If the task to be assessed is substantial, difficult or complex then, in all probability, it will not be practical or effective to carry out a single risk assessment to cover the whole of the work. The job will need to be broken down into separate elements or work, each of which will have to be assessed separately.

Alternatively, it should be possible to cover the whole of a relatively straightforward job (such as retiling a house) with a single risk assessment.

The process of practical risk assessment has no fixed rules on how it should be undertaken, or how risk assessments should be structured or laid out. Each company will decide upon what suits its needs. The process for developing risk assessments should not be over-complicated. The simpler the process, the less likely that anything will be overlooked. It may need input from both management and employees, and should address the points below.

- ☑ What is going to be done? (This should include plant, equipment, people, materials and the working environment.)
- ☑ How exactly is the activity to be carried out (for example, what plant and competences are required)?
- ☑ Where and when is the work to be done?
- ☑ How could this work affect employees and other people?
- ☑ What risk control measures are already in place?
- ☑ Is the level of risk to health or safety acceptable?
- ☑ What additional risk control measures are necessary?

The above approach to the identification of all relevant hazards associated with the work will address the following.

- ☑ The likelihood of injury or harm arising to employees and others who may be affected by the work.
- ☑ Any other specific legal requirements.
- ☑ All of the risks.
- ☑ The necessary control measure to eliminate or reduce health and safety risks associated with the work hierarchy of preventative and protective measures.
- ☑ The information needed for those involved or affected by the work.

5.8.1 What do you do after your risk assessment as an employer?

- ☑ Put into effect the measures that you have decided will adequately control the risks.
- ☑ Communicate the findings of your risk assessments, particularly details of the hazards identified and what control measures are in place, to anyone who needs to know (for example, the main (or principal) contractor, your employees and sub-contractors).
- ☑ It is most important that the findings of risk assessments are communicated to anyone whose health and/or safety is likely to be affected by the job. Do not just store them away!

5.8.2 What should a supervisor do after they receive a risk assessment?

- ☑ They should speak to the site manager on a regular basis.
- ☑ Check that the risk control measures to be put in place are right for the work situation.
- ☑ Seek clarification of uncertainties and make their manager aware of any findings of a point of work risk assessment so that control measures are corrected.
- ☑ Before briefing their work team ensure the risk assessments and method statements are correct for the site specifics.
- ☑ Explain the risk assessments and method statements to their work team, ensure understanding (by asking questions) and record the names of those briefed (and when).

5.9 Communication

Those people physically carrying out the task should be consulted in the assessment process as they can have valuable knowledge and experience. By being involved, they have effectively bought into and better appreciate the risks and the control measures needed, and thus are more likely to follow them.

5.9.1 Documentation

In many cases the person completing the risk assessment is not the person doing or directly supervising the work.

There are many types of documentation with varying levels of complexity and length of content. Whilst a risk assessment or method statement is technically correct, it may be that it is in a format that is too complicated or long for an operative to take in.

Asking the workforce to read pages and pages of text and to obtain a signature to say they have read and understood the content before they start work is not helpful in achieving a safe and healthy workplace.

If the workforce do not read everything provided, they will not appreciate the risk involved in the activity, and so will not appreciate the consequences of not incorporating the control measures required, or understand why they are required, therefore continuing to work as they always have.

It may therefore be necessary to convert the findings of a risk assessment into a simpler document, both in terms of terminology and layout, which relates to what the workforce must do. Consideration should be given to the use of images or sketches of what is needed (such as a slinging arrangement or pictures of respiratory protective equipment (RPE) being used correctly).

Involving the workforce in the risk assessment process is vital in developing a safe system of work that they feel comfortable with. It may well be that their preferred or alternative method of working is quicker and easier, but it has (or has not got) additional risks. This can then be assessed and any necessary working practices amended and agreed, so the workforce and their supervisors know they are following the risk assessment or method statement.

5.9.2 Language difficulties

The needs of any site workers who have poor, or no, understanding of either written or spoken English must be taken into account when compiling and communicating risk assessments. Consideration also needs to be given to how workers will be communicated with to ensure they are engaged and consulted with.

Effective communication is an essential element of controlling risk; how such communication can be established must be a priority where there is the potential for language difficulties on site. A control measure that could be put into place is to ensure that the supervisor is able to effectively communicate with the workers or ensure that the non-English worker works with someone who can speak their language and interpret for them.

5.9.3 Worker engagement in practice

HSE Health & Safety Executive

The construction section of the HSE website contains information on risk assessments and a series of worker engagement case studies. It also has a London 2012 games, Lessons for Industry, section that includes the following case study about the use of photographs in method statements.

London 2012 Olympic and Paralympic Games

Example of one of the photographs used in the method statement

Background. Involving your workforce means much more than simply giving instructions. It means sharing information and involving the workforce in finding solutions to reduce health and safety risks.

Issue. Ensuring that your workers understand method statements for complex, high risk work.

Solution. A specialist contractor had to install 12,000 seats in the basketball arena to a tight deadline. The contractor wrote the method statement (MS) for the installation process. A small team tested the MS on a practice run using a model unit in site-specific conditions. Following feedback, the contractor modified the MS and then rolled it out to the entire workforce.

As a result of the early engagement, the MS was modified to include diagrams to explain processes and instructions, a map of the sequence of build, and photographs of work in action. The MS also changed as workers and teams discussed progress at the most important stages of the project. Changes and modifications were agreed with the workforce before they were put in place.

5.10 Method statements

A method statement is a document prepared by an organisation that describes in a logical sequence exactly how a work activity is to be carried out in a manner which is safe and without risk to health.

To a large extent, the way that the job will be undertaken, and therefore detailed in the method statement, will reflect the findings of the risk assessment(s) for the same job. The means selected for controlling risk will influence the method of carrying out the job. In most cases, extensive reference to the risk assessment(s) will be necessary during the drafting of a method statement.

Well written method statements provide an ideal means of communicating vital health and safety information to those who will be doing the work and others (such as contractors) who have an interest in how the job will be carried out.

For routine and repetitive activities (work that is carried out many times where the hazards and risk are the same) a previous method statement may be applied, again provided it has been reviewed at point of work (by the supervisor) to ensure that it is still relevant. This is sometimes called a **generic method statement**.

Where the work is new, more complicated or unusual then a **specific method statement** will need to be produced. This can be a generic method statement updated to take the new situation into account. It should then be used to ensure that the work is carried out safely, properly and in the proper order.

For method statement guidance refer to Appendix B.

5.11 Permit to work

Whilst there is no requirement in law to use a permit to work system, they are often used to regulate how potentially high-risk activities are to be carried out in a healthy and safe manner. As such, they very much support the risk assessment from which they are derived.

Permits to work are often, but not exclusively, required in the following situations.

- If it involves entry into a confined space.
- When it depends upon the isolation of high-voltage electrical equipment.
- If it involves the disturbance of any system carrying a fluid or gas under pressure.
- If it involves hot works.

A permit to work is a formal, dated and time-limited certificate signed by a properly authorised and competent person. Receipt of a permit is acknowledged by the signature of the person in charge of the work, who will retain a copy; another copy will be retained by the person issuing the permit to work.

Other signatures on the permit will certify that any control measures necessary for the job to start have been implemented (for example, locking-out an electrical supply or checking the atmosphere in a confined space). A permit will indicate the time and date at which it expires. If the work is not completed at that time, depending upon the circumstances:

- it is usually necessary to make everything safe, for everyone to leave the work area before the permit expires and for the permit to be cancelled
- it may be safe to extend the expiry time and for the work area to be reoccupied.

When the work is completed, or the expiry time has passed, the person in charge of the work must return their copy of the permit to the person who issued it and the permit is cancelled.

5.12 CITB risk assessment and method statement manager

This popular CD-ROM enables users to produce, print and store task-specific risk assessments and method statements as required under the Management of Health and Safety at Work Regulations and other legislation.

- Save and retrieve previous risk assessments and update them as necessary, either within the programme or as standalone Word documents.
- Pre-populated common hazards and risk controls in drop-down menus.
- Facility to add site-specific hazards, methodology and risk controls.
- Risk assessment and method statement templates, which include:
  - fields for the signing and dating of each document by hand
  - the facility for adding footers to all pages
  - a facility for identifying the owner of each hazard and an action-by date.
- Option to produce a related or standalone method statement.
- Includes a *Guide to risk assessment* document, which may be downloaded and printed as a continuing reference.

It is essential for business owners, managers, supervisors and health and safety professionals.

www.

For more information on this and other products visit the CITB website.

Appendix A – The HSE's example risk assessment for a plastering company

HSE

Health and Safety Executive

Example risk assessment for a plastering company

Setting the scene

The manager of a plastering company carried out a general risk assessment that covered their typical work. The deputy manager and the employee safety representative also helped. The risk assessment was used to help manage health and safety at the firm, and when tendering for contracts to demonstrate the firm's approach to health and safety. This meant that in the tender documents it was made clear exactly what was needed from the principal contractor to do the job safely and properly.

The firm won the plastering contract for a development of a three-storey block of flats. Work was due to start on 1 May 2007. The manager checked the construction phase plan and met the principal contractor's site manager on the site. One of the issues they considered was the sequencing and logistics of the work, alongside that of other fit-out trades, to ensure safe access and working arrangements for all. Another was the issue of fatigue, and the number of work breaks that were needed.

Important reminder

This example risk assessment shows the kind of approach a small business might take. Use it as a guide to think through some of the hazards in your business and the steps you need to take to control the risks. Please note that it is not a generic risk assessment that you can just put your company name on and adopt wholesale without any thought. This would not satisfy the law – and would not be effective in protecting people.

Every business is different – you need to think through the hazards and controls required in your business for yourself.

This extra information helped the manager to decide whether the general risk assessment covered all the hazards and risks expected in this job. If it did not, it would need to be amended to make the general risk assessment specific to the work and conditions of this job.

However, the manager decided that for this job his general risk assessment did cover all the expected risks and that therefore no additional paperwork was needed.

How was the risk assessment done?

To produce his general risk assessment, the manager followed the guidance in *Five steps to risk assessment* (www.hse.gov.uk/pubns/indg163.pdf).

1 To identify the hazards the manager:

- used training and experience of similar work;
- took into account the rules of most construction sites; and
- looked at HSE's website for free health and safety advice and guidance for the construction industry.

2 The manager wrote down who would be harmed by the hazards and how.

3 He considered the risks of each hazard and decided what was needed to control those risks.

4 He discussed the findings with the deputy manager and the safety representative. He then put the risk assessment into practice, writing down who was responsible for doing what, and by when. When each action was completed, it was ticked off and the date recorded.

5 The manager told staff about the risk assessment, explaining that the risks identified were common to most plastering jobs and would be put into practice and the control measures identified would be put into place for all company jobs.

6 However, the manager also said that all sites were different and that extra risk controls might be needed at some jobs. This would be considered during site visits before each job started, and staff are to be made aware of any additional risks and what needs to be done to control those risks.

7 One of the workers did not speak English. The manager had planned for this, having previously arranged with the site manager for another worker, who was bi-lingual in the relevant language, to translate.

Example risk assessment: Plastering company

1 of 3 pages

Health and Safety Executive

Company name: Smith's Plastering **Date of risk assessment:** 1 March 2007

(revised to be specific for internal plastering of three-storey flats job, 23 April 2007)

What are the hazards?	Who might be harmed and how?	What are you already doing?	What further action is necessary?	Action by whom?	Action by when?	Done
Falling from height	Serious or even fatal injury could occur if an operator falls from height. Others working below also at risk.	■ Sufficient Step-Ups available, all in good condition. ■ Platform trellis, with guardrail, used for stairwells and operators are trained in how to put it up, use and dismantle it. ■ Stairs and landings have handrails.	■ Include work at height in toolbox talk before beginning work on day one.	Site Manager Foreman	1/5/07	
Slips and trips	All operators, and tradesmen nearby, may suffer sprains, bruising or fractures if they trip over objects, such as work debris, or slip on spillages.	■ All operators wear safety boots – 'no boots, no job' policy. ■ Good housekeeping, eg debris such as plaster bags put in skip, brush available to use to keep work area clear. ■ All trailing cables in work area hung up or otherwise kept out of harm's way. ■ Safe route to job agreed with site manager based on site health and safety plan.	■ Manager to check on-site housekeeping during visits.	Site Manager	From 1/5/07	
			■ Include in toolbox talk before beginning work on day one.	Site Manager	From 1/5/07	
Workplace transport	Operators risk serious or even fatal injuries from moving vehicles on site – particularly when reversing.	■ Safe route to workplace, and to welfare facilities, agreed with site manager based on site health and safety plan. ■ Staff know that they must never move vehicles on a site unless authorised by site manager. ■ Staff wear high-visibility tabards while on site.	■ Include in toolbox talk before beginning work on day one.	Site Manager Foreman	1/5/07	
Manual handling	Operators risk injury, particularly to the back, from lifting and handling heavy or awkward objects, eg, plasterboard, and from repetitive strain problems from plastering.	■ Dry plaster mix lifted to the work areas using a hoist supplied by the site manager and operated by a competent person. ■ Dry plaster mix supplied in bags weighing less than 25 kg. ■ Plasterboard for ceilings is of smallest size practicable. ■ Operators know and follow safe system of work for fitting plasterboard to ceiling, including knowledge of maximum weight for an individual manual lift. ■ Job rotation between ceiling and walls.	■ Remind operators of plasterboard safe system of work at toolbox talk.	Site Manager Foreman	1/5/07	

Example risk assessment: Plastering company

2 of 3 pages

HSE

Health and Safety Executive

What are the hazards?	Who might be harmed and how?	What are you already doing?	What further action is necessary?	Action by whom?	Action by when?	Done
Hazardous substances Dry plaster mix	Operators and nearby tradesmen at risk from dry plaster powder which may irritate eyes or sensitive skin, or cause short-term irritation of respiratory system.	■ Operators know the risks of dry plaster powder and know to avoid skin contact, excessive dust build-up and contact with eyes. ■ Work area suitable to prevent excessive dust build-up. ■ Water supply nearby to wash dust off skin. ■ Operators wear eye protection when plastering ceilings. ■ Operators keep work area clean. ■ Gloves and barrier creams available.	■ At toolbox talk, remind operators of risks of dry plaster powder, and to wear gloves, eye protection and dust masks when emptying sacks and preparing the mix.	Manager	1/5/07	
Electricity	Operators and others risk potentially fatal injuries if they receive a shock from faulty electrical equipment and/or installation.	■ Site manager will arrange for permanent electric supply to be turned off while plastering work ongoing. ■ Site manager to supply 110 v temporary supply. ■ Staff know to check all cables, leads etc of all powered tools/ equipment before use, and to report all faults to their supervisor.	■ At toolbox talk on day one, manager to reinforce rules on electrical safety.	Manager	1/5/07	
Welfare	Good welfare facilities reduce risk of dermatitis, help good hygiene etc.	■ Agreement with site manager that staff may use site welfare facilities – toilets, washing facilities with hot and cold water and mess room/kitchen.	■ Tell staff about facilities at toolbox talk on day one.	Manager	1/5/07	

Assessment review date: 1/7/08

Example risk assessment: Plastering company
Published by the Health and Safety Executive 11/08

3 of 3 pages

A 05

Appendix B – Method statement guidance

Method statements should be written clearly to enable those doing the work to fully understand the details of the job and its health and safety requirements. The suggested content for a method statement is outlined below.

If the work is of a simple or minor nature, a simplified form of method statement may be more appropriate. Alternatively, it may be preferable to use the format below but to annotate inappropriate fields as 'Not applicable'.

Validity	Insert the issue number of the method statement and brief details of the changes associated with each new issue. Identify the intended start and finish dates.
Hazards	List the known hazards associated with the work, as identified by the risk assessment.
Means of access	Identify: ■ locations of work (for example at height or in excavations) ■ access equipment required ■ specialist contractors involved.
Work details	Outline: ■ the limits of the work covered by this method statement ■ in a logical order, the list of work that makes up the whole job, indicating how health and safety issues will be addressed for identified hazards, including the protection of other trades.
Permits to work	Describe: ■ which tasks will be controlled by a permit to work (for example hot works, access to risers and work in confined spaces) ■ who will issue and co-ordinate the permits.
Supervision	Identify who will supervise the job and, if necessary, who will supervise different parts of the job.
Workforce details	Identify: ■ the specific labour required to carry out the job in a safe and healthy manner ■ any special training or skills required ■ details of competence cards held.
Health and safety monitoring	Specify how day-to-day standards of health and safety will be monitored and controlled.
Plant inspection and operator training	Identify: ■ what items of plant and equipment will be used ■ operators' experience/qualifications ■ thorough examination and maintenance details.
Disconnection/reconnection of services	Identify: ■ which services must be isolated/reconnected ■ who will carry out the work ■ methods of locating underground services ■ who will certify that the services have been isolated/reconnected.
Hazardous substances	Identify: ■ the hazardous substances that will be used or disturbed ■ how those affected will be informed of the health hazards ■ the protective measures to be used ■ details of any sampling that may be required.
Occupational health assessments	Identify: ■ which works will require health surveillance for the operatives carrying them out ■ which operatives are affected ■ who will arrange for the health surveillance ■ who will carry out the health surveillance.
Personal protective equipment	Identify: ■ which items of PPE/RPE will be used, for which training will be required ■ who is responsible for arranging the training ■ who will carry out the training.

Emergency procedures	Identify: ■ possible causes of emergency or site evacuation ■ how emergency procedures will be communicated ■ who is responsible for calling the emergency services ■ contact details for out-of-hours emergencies.
Environmental controls	Describe: ■ threats to the environment arising from the work ■ which environmental protection measures will be put in place ■ how different types of waste will be stored and disposed of.
Safety of the public and occupiers	Identify who will ensure that the health and safety of the public and other occupiers will be protected. Describe how the health and safety of the public, including, if necessary, the occupiers of the building, will be protected.
Public nuisance	Identify: ■ possible sources of nuisance for neighbouring people/properties ■ who will be responsible for neighbourhood liaison.
Briefing register	List by name those people to whom the method statement has been explained and consider including a signature block to indicate that the content has been understood.

For a method statement form refer to Section G: *Checklists and forms*.

A
05

06

Induction and training

Contents

Supporting information

G: Checklists and forms

GT 700 Toolbox talks

Overview

Construction and building sites can be dangerous places to work, even for experienced workers. It is a legal requirement to give everyone on site, whether new to the industry, experienced or even a temporary visitor, basic information about the site so they can remain safe. This is usually done in the form of a site induction and can vary in style, delivery method and length depending upon factors such as company induction procedures, location and size of site, type of work and client requirements.

Whatever the content, it is important that those attending understand it and that it is specific to the site.

This chapter explains why site inductions and training are important and offers some suggested content and strategy.

6.1 Introduction

It is a requirement of health and safety law that employees are provided with health and safety training whenever they are exposed to new or increased risks.

When employees first arrive in the company or at a new site, this training takes the form of an induction. It is a legal requirement under the **Construction (Design and Management) Regulations** (CDM) that principal contractors and, where applicable, contractors must ensure a suitable site induction is provided. It is accepted that providing proper and effective health and safety induction training can have a significant impact on the likelihood of accidents and injuries during a person's first few days, weeks or months with a company or on a particular site.

Given that every accident occurring to an employee can be seen as an eventual financial cost to the employer, then anything that can be done to reduce accidents is of direct financial benefit to the employer. The costs of giving proper and effective health and safety induction training are relatively minor when viewed as one of the cost benefits that can accrue from accident avoidance and prevention. This also applies to the prevention of long-term ill health and the avoidance of dangerous occurrences.

6.2 Important points

- ☑ Everyone arriving on a new site, whether new to the industry, experienced or even a temporary visitor, should be given an induction to the site.
- ☑ Accident statistics show that the chances of accidents happening to people are increased during their first few days on site.
- ☑ The threats to health and safety will vary from site to site and even on the same site as work progresses and the hazards change.
- ☑ An effective induction process is an essential part of on-site health and safety management.
- ☑ The content of the induction presentation must:
  - be understandable, comprehensive and relevant to the hazards present on site at that time
  - anticipate and inform inductees of forthcoming changes to the hazards on site
  - allow for the effective induction of inductees who do not have English as their first language or may otherwise have difficulty in understanding what is being said.
- ☑ The CDM Regulations place a specific duty on contractors and/or principal contractors (where appointed) to provide all of their workers with a site induction.

6.3 Induction requirements

There are two types of induction contained within this chapter: induction training and site inductions.

6.3.1 Induction training

Induction training is for new employees or for training existing employees in new topics or risks.

The Management of Health and Safety at Work Regulations require every employer to ensure that employees are provided with adequate health and safety training in the following situations.

- ☑ During recruitment into the employer's undertaking.
- ☑ When exposed to new or increased risks because:
  - they have been transferred or given a change of responsibilities within the employer's undertaking
  - of the introduction of new work equipment or a change regarding work equipment already in use within the employer's undertaking
  - of the introduction of new technology into the employer's undertaking
  - of the introduction of a new system of work or a change regarding a system of work already in use within the employer's undertaking.

6.3.2 Site inductions

The Construction (Design and Management) Regulations specifically require the following.

- That the principal contractor must ensure a suitable site induction is provided to every site worker.
- That contractors provide all of their workers with the information and training that is necessary for their health and safety, including a suitable site induction, where it is not provided by a principal contractor.

The above requirement on contractors to provide site inductions means that inductions must be carried out on any type, size and duration of a project. The requirements of other regulations, which in themselves indicate a need for competence in certain work situations, when viewed against the type of work to be carried out, might indicate additional topics that need to be covered during site induction.

6.3.3 Responsibilities of employers and employees

To assist in preparation and delivery of induction training, an aide-memoire of the responsibilities of employers and employees can be found in Appendices B and C. This could also help training providers with any questions that may arise during or after an induction training programme.

It will be for the employer to decide when and where the training takes place. Induction training should take place before anyone starts work and when they are new to site. It is important that the induction training is seen as a formal company procedure, which the company provides for the benefit of the inductee, so that the employer can be seen to be meeting both the letter and the spirit of the law. If it is seen as 'something that is just necessary, we have to do it anyway' then it will fail to have the desired long-term effects.

The style and content of the presentation will vary between company and site. However, the person giving the presentation needs to have both the necessary skills and knowledge, together with the ability or presence to deliver the programme effectively and in a meaningful manner.

6.4 Types of inductees

Mention of the word *induction* or *inductee* would cause many people to think of a person arriving on site or into the company totally new. Whilst this is the case for some people, there will be a significant number of people who do not fall into this category. In wider terms the following could also be referred to as inductees.

- Young people joining the industry for the first time (this will generally be persons joining a company as trainees or apprentices).
- Persons arriving at a new site even though they have been in the industry for some time.
- Persons transferring between companies within the industry.
- Persons who have been promoted (for example, from tradesperson to chargehand).
- Employees who have been given different responsibilities (for example, employees who have successfully gained CPCS cards for specific items of plant and will now be driving plant on site as opposed to their former occupation).
- Those who do not regularly work on the site but visit occasionally (for example, architects or students).

The inductions should be proportionate to the nature of the visit.

It must be appreciated that different types of inductee will probably require different levels or styles of induction training because of their varying levels of knowledge, experience and competence within the industry. It is only if, after induction, they have all the appropriate information as regards company policy and site rules (including the principal contractor's site rules, where applicable) that they will be able to integrate into the workforce and work without risks to their own health and safety or to others who may be affected.

Escorted visitors only need to be made aware of the main hazards and control measures.

6.5 Induction difficulties

It is essential that the health and safety messages put across during site induction are fully understood. Possible barriers to learning will depend largely upon the training methods used. For example, reliance on written training materials will disadvantage those with dyslexia or other reading difficulties. Similarly, an increasing number of workers do not speak English as their first language, and some may find induction training of limited value if it is not delivered with this in mind.

www.

For examples of images that can be used to assist during an induction refer to the companion website.

The person organising the training should establish the limitations of those undertaking induction, remembering that some inductees may be embarrassed about their limitations and so reluctant to admit them.

To successfully induct those whose first language is not English, but who have some understanding, it will probably be necessary to modify the presentation in style, speed of delivery and the aids used. Induction aids may need to be more visual, with less reliance upon the written word. Where there are operatives who do not speak English at all, it is likely that specialist help, such as interpreters, will be required. There may also be scope for training someone on the site who speaks both languages to carry out specific induction sessions for specific groups.

Encouragement should be given to those who have reading, writing or language difficulties to seek help from the learning support unit of the local college of higher and further education, or any in-house training arrangements that exist.

Whatever the reason for any inductee experiencing difficulty in understanding what they have been told, all inductees must be given the opportunity to ask for any point to be explained again or in different terms.

For further information refer to Chapter A07 Communication with non-English speaking workers.

6.6 Induction content

Different companies will have different issues to include in the induction training. The requirements will vary as work on the site progresses. In the early days there may be demolition, excavations and other problems at ground level. As the site and above-ground works progress, the hazards will change and it will be necessary for the emphasis in the health and safety training to change.

As the site develops, temporary or permanent traffic routes may be introduced, or the circulation of traffic on site may need to change (for example, due to the repositioning of a crane or the installation of services). All these issues should be reflected in the induction training that will be provided for people arriving on site or as the project progresses. It is quite possible, or even likely, that the induction session delivered on day one of the project will not be valid after three months.

Part of the induction process must be to find out what the audience already knows, to identify the most important areas that must be covered and use plain language, illustrating with diagrams, drawings and pictures to ensure that inductees can easily take in the information.

At the end of the induction session, explain to the inductees that they will all be required to add their name and signature to an attendance sheet signifying that they have understood what they have been told.

The induction should be site specific and highlight risks and control measures. The following should be considered.

- ☑ Outline of the project.
- ☑ Management of the project.
- ☑ First aid arrangements.
- ☑ Accident and incident reporting arrangements.
- ☑ Arrangements for briefing workers on an ongoing basis (such as noticeboards and toolbox talks).
- ☑ Individuals' responsibility for health and safety.

This chapter contains some of the suggested topics and other examples that should be considered when induction training is to be given. It is not suggested that all are relevant to all sites or that issues relevant to more than one site should be given the same weighting. They are given as an indication of subject areas that need to be covered – the depth to which they are covered will depend upon site conditions. There will undoubtedly be other issues that are specific to a company or site and these will need to be considered and developed by the company concerned.

Appendix A contains a list of topics that should be considered for site induction content, together with a brief explanation of each. Obviously, users will amend the content in order to reflect the philosophy of their company, site or organisation regarding health, safety and welfare provisions. There may be items covered that you feel are inappropriate and these should be omitted.

Conversely, some additional items not covered may be of particular importance to your company, site or organisation and these should be included. The comments made are of a very general nature and do not attempt to explain the specific requirements of legislation. It is thought that at an induction training session participants do not need to be told specific titles of regulations. However, users can include them if they wish to.

Refer to the HSE website for an induction presentation template aimed at smaller construction companies.

6.7 Competency and card schemes

6.7.1 Competence

In 2011, following consultation with industry, a report was produced for the HSE that looked at the construction industry routes to competence, including all the different competency card schemes.

The report can be downloaded free from the research section of the HSE website.

6.7.2 Behavioural competence

The report supported a need for a broader definition of competence to include not just job competence and (above-basic) health and safety awareness, but a third strand of behavioural competence.

This behavioural competence includes self-awareness, risk awareness and situational awareness.

Behavioural competence

Behavioural awareness comprises those individual behaviours, attitudes, self-awareness and limitations that impact upon performance and safety at work. It covers the interaction between people and the environment in which they work, the equipment they use, and the procedures and techniques they use. The objectives of behavioural competence are enhanced effectiveness and safety.

This expanded definition of competence is tripartite and should include the following.

- **Occupational skills.**
- Deep and relevant **knowledge and understanding**.
- Ongoing evidence of **appropriate behaviours and attitudes**, to be embedded at all levels.

6.7.3 Supervisor and management competence

The report went on to say that qualifications should be enhanced to include mentoring and coaching skills in behavioural competence. In the coming years many of the recommendations from the report will be incorporated into qualifications, training courses and development programmes for supervisors and management, such as those listed below.

- Alignment to new definitions of competence, behaviours and attitudes.
- A greater focus on **taught** qualifications whereby the basis of the input of knowledge is on risk, causation, person-management skills and situational awareness.
- Continued professional development (CPD) (a necessary aspect and a fundamental component).
- Opportunity to train people in roles to be effective assessors of staff.

For details of courses, training programmes or further information on competency refer to the CITB website.

Other relevant construction organisations are listed below, where further supporting information can be found.

- ConstructionSkills (NI).
- Construction Employers Federation Limited (CEF NI).
- Construction Industry Confederation (CIC).
- Construction Plant-hire Association (CPA).
- Federation of Master Builders (FMB).
- Health and Safety Executive (HSE).
- Heating and Ventilating Contractors' Association (HVCA).
- Joint Industry Board for Plumbing Mechanical Engineering Services (JIB-PMES).
- Lift and Escalator Industry Association (LEIA).
- National Access and Scaffolding Confederation (NASC).
- National Demolition Training Group (NDTG).
- Scottish and Northern Ireland Joint Industry Board for the Plumbing Industry (SNIJIB).
- Strategic Forum for Construction (SFfC).
- TunnelSkills.
- UK Contractors Group (UKCG).
- Union of Construction, Allied Trades and Technicians (UCATT).
- Unison.
- Unite.

6.7.4 Card schemes

Access to construction sites may require a relevant scheme card, which are shown in the table on the following page. Different schemes exist in different professions but all card schemes have similar requirements, such as an NVQ or SVQ and a CITB *Health, safety and environment test*.

General	CSCS	Construction Skills Certification Scheme.
	CSR	Construction Skills Registration (Northern Ireland).
Plant operatives	CPCS	Construction Plant Competence Scheme.
Demolition operatives	CCDO	Certificate of Competence of Demolition Operatives.
Scaffolders	CISRS	Construction Industry Scaffolders Record Scheme.
HVACR operatives	ESS	Engineering Services SKILLcard.
Plumbers	JIBPMES	Joint Industry Board for Plumbing and Mechanical Services.
	SNIJIB	Scottish and Northern Ireland Joint Industry Board.
Electricians	ECS	Electrotechnical Certification Scheme.

www. **For more information on card schemes, refer to the CITB website.**

A 06

6.7.5 Health, safety and environment test

The CITB *Health, safety and environment test* helps raise standards across the industry. It ensures that workers meet a minimum level of health, safety and environmental awareness before going on site.

It should be used as a stepping stone, encouraging employers and their workforce to go on and develop their knowledge even further.

The test has been running for over 10 years and it underwent significant improvements in early 2012. These improvements included an enhanced test and a new delivery infrastructure. The test was further refreshed for a 2015 release, to reflect the implementation of the new CDM Regulations.

All tests last for 45 minutes and have 50 multiple-choice questions including:

- ☑ 12 behavioural case study questions about how to behave on a construction site to stay healthy and safe, followed by
- ☑ 38 knowledge questions to check knowledge of health, safety and environment issues.

Different tests have been developed to meet the demands of different trades and professions. The following tests are available.

- ☑ Operative test.
- ☑ Specialist tests.
- ☑ Managers' and professionals' test.

www. **For more information about the test and how to prepare, refer to the CITB website.**

6.8 Records

It is extremely important that records are kept showing which workers have attended site induction, together with details of the training they have received and the date it was carried out.

This will enable employers to demonstrate to the Health and Safety Executive, the client, the principal contractor and other interested parties that they have complied with the requirements of legislation and that they are committed to ensuring the health and safety of their employees and any others who may be affected.

Such records could help prove that health and safety induction training was given, should there be a legal challenge.

6.8.1 Site induction register

For an example of a site induction register that can be copied and used for record purposes on induction training refer to Section G: *Checklists and forms*.

6.8.2 Induction training checklist

For an example of an induction training checklist, which can be attached to the induction attendance list as a record of which topics were covered and used by the trainer to ensure that the important basic facts are included in an induction training talk refer to Section G: *Checklists and forms*.

6.9 Ongoing training

Once the employee has been inducted to the site, and/or into the organisation, the company should ensure a training programme is implemented to help employees develop their knowledge, skills and attitudes, to ensure they are competent in health and safety aspects of their work.

A company could choose to implement a training cycle, which has six phases.

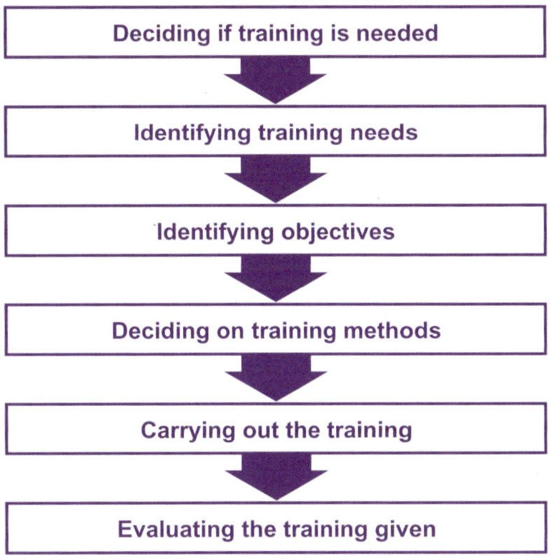

6.9.1 Deciding if training is needed

- ☑ Use information from job specifications, known abilities, experience and previous training records.
- ☑ Compare data against what the organisation requires the individual to know and to be able to do.
- ☑ Any variation between the two reveals a potential training requirement.

6.9.2 Identifying training needs

- ☑ Look at accident and health records and determine training requirements linked to causes and preventative means.
- ☑ Discuss procedures, materials and use of tools and equipment with employees to establish their understanding and highlight any skills gap.
- ☑ Observe and question employees whilst they are performing their roles and responsibilities.

6.9.3 Identifying objectives

- ☑ Clarify what the targeted employees should learn through their training.
- ☑ Evaluate the effectiveness of the training programme.

6.9.4 Deciding on training methods

- ☑ Organise training either internally or through external training providers.
- ☑ Ensure trainers are qualified and competent in their subject field.
- ☑ Trainers should encourage the fullest participation by the trainees.

6.9.5 Carrying out the training

- On-the-job training can generate new risks. Therefore off-site training, in some instances, may have to be completed.
- Use internal resources or external organisations.

6.9.6 Evaluating the training given

- Determine if the training has achieved the objectives.
- Establish if training has been worth the money and time spent on delivery and attendance.
- The training plan, structure, content and methods may be subject to revision, following evaluation.

6.10 Promoting health and safety training

Health and safety training is sometimes viewed with suspicion, and those identified as requiring training can feel they are being picked on, or that their performance is thought to be substandard. Incentives (such as promotion or increased pay), applicable to some forms of training, do not generally result from health and safety training.

Managers should encourage their employees to engage willingly and positively in such training. This task can be even more difficult in organisations with limited training history.

The following points may help in the initial planning stage of training.

- Encourage employees' genuine participation.
- Raise their awareness of the employer and employee responsibilities.
- Use relevant sector examples to illustrate the consequences of inadequate health and safety training.
- Inform employees about the organisation's training policy, including how individuals are chosen for training.
- Make arrangements for payment of wages or salaries during training, or reimbursements of expenses or fees paid.
- Support and reassure those who may lack confidence, especially those who have not attended training since leaving education.
- Emphasise the value to everyone concerned of the short and long-term benefits of a working life free from injury and ill health.

A
06

www.

Refer to the CITB website for advice on a full range of health and safety training.

Worker loses sight in one eye due to insufficient training

A company has been fined after a worker lost his sight in one eye when a compressed air hose whipped him in the face while he was carrying out maintenance work to clean a paint fume filter.

When he had finished, he isolated the compressed air supply at the connection point and went to disconnect the equipment. However, he was unaware the pressure from the flexible hose needed venting before disconnection and, as a result, the hose whipped and struck him in the face, hitting his eye and breaking his cheekbone.

The 49-year-old injured man permanently lost the sight in his right eye but he has been able to return to work.

The HSE investigation found the company had failed to provide the worker with sufficient information, instruction or training on the equipment he was using when the incident happened. The company pleaded guilty to breaching Section 2(1) of the Health and Safety at Work Act 1974. They were fined £20,000 and ordered to pay £7,813.70 in costs.

After the hearing, the HSE inspector said: 'This was an entirely preventable incident that has resulted in a worker losing his sight in one eye – an injury which will affect him permanently.

The sudden release of compressed air is a known hazard in industry. (The company) should have ensured that there was a safe system of work in place and that anyone working with compressed air had been given sufficient information, instruction and training to keep themselves and others safe from air blasts and whipping or snaking hoses'.

Appendix A – Site induction topics

Access

Explain the rules regarding access to, and egress from, the workplace. Are there any one-way systems? Are there any prohibited areas? Are there any special rules or conditions applying to the site or workplace?

Accident reporting

The participants should be in no doubt of the requirements for reporting accidents. Explain when, where and to whom accidents must be reported and, in general, how they will be investigated. Your procedures may go beyond those required by legislation as a company policy decision.

Alcohol and drugs

Explain the rules or company policy about arriving or being on site under the influence of alcohol or drugs, or consuming them during the hours of employment, including action that will be taken. There may be a policy of random testing and this should also be explained.

The issue of prescribed drugs should also be covered as some of these can have side effects, such as drowsiness. If the user is authorised to operate plant or drive vehicles, this needs to be addressed and resolved with the supervisor or management.

Asbestos

If the project is a new build on a greenfield site then the probability of finding asbestos is very remote. If, however, the project is on a brownfield site, there may be asbestos in the ground, and if carrying out a refurbishment or renovation then there is significant chance of discovering asbestos within the existing structure. If asbestos or asbestos-containing materials are potentially present, it is essential to provide elementary asbestos awareness training, including details of any prohibited areas, to reflect the site conditions.

You should have a company policy for dealing with any material suspected of being asbestos and employees should be informed of this policy.

Assembly points

See also **emergency procedure**. Explain where the assembly points are for site evacuation in the event of an emergency.

Boundaries

Explain the boundaries of the site if there is no perimeter fence. Include the prevention of trespass.

CDM Regulations

Explain any appropriate on-site rules, the provisions the principal contractor has made for consultation with the workforce and where the statutory notice F10 is displayed.

Competence

You may need to advise employees and others of the levels of competence required for operating certain types of plant or carrying out particular pieces of work. See also **registration schemes**.

Confidential issues

Explain the provision for 'whistle blowing'. Also how employees can raise confidential (including medical) issues if the need arises.

Confined spaces

Explain the rules that apply on site. Many employees will fail to recognise that a confined space can be above ground, or be as innocuous as a sub-basement boiler room. Unfortunately, confined spaces have been responsible for a number of deaths in the industry, all of which could have been avoided by compliance with proper health and safety procedures.

Consultation with employees

It is a legal requirement to consult with employees, which should be two-way. The questions that you should address during induction include:

- ☑ what the mechanism is for workers to bring any health and safety concerns they have to the attention of site management
- ☑ if there is a health and safety committee on site and, if so, who the members are
- ☑ if there are any trade union-appointed representatives and, if so, who they are.

If there is a suggestion box or scheme, explain how employees can put forward ideas for improvements in health, safety and welfare, waste minimisation and so on, on a day-by-day basis.

Contamination

The raised awareness of environmental matters makes the prevention of ground contamination of growing importance. Explain how employees can prevent spillage of diesel fuel, paint, oil, thinners, cement, concrete or any other substance that could lead to contamination.

Control of Substances Hazardous to Health (COSHH)

Explain the on-site procedures relating to hazardous substances. Are there any substances that are additional to the usual cement, oils, paints, and so on?

Competency card schemes (CSCS cards)

Explain the requirements for CSCS and other cards. See also **registration schemes**.

Dangerous occurrences

Explain the policy in relation to the reporting of dangerous occurrences. It is thought that many go unreported as employees regard them as an accident where nobody was injured. Given that this could lead to a company being prosecuted for failing to report a dangerous occurrence, it is important that the appropriate instructions are given at induction training sessions.

Dermatitis

Explain that contact dermatitis can be caused by some relatively common substances (such as diesel and mould release oil, paints, thinners and cement). Gloves should be worn on appropriate occasions, and barrier creams should be used properly.

These occasions should have been identified by the employer risk assessments.

Discipline

Explain the company policy regarding breaches of health and safety legislation, site or company rules.

Dress code

Explain the effects of sun exposure and the importance of preventing skin cancer. Explain company or site rules on whether shorts or sleeveless vests are permissible on site.

Drying rooms

Explain the location and use of drying rooms. Include who is responsible for maintaining cleanliness, tidiness and disposal of abandoned clothing and equipment.

Edge protection

Explain the standard that is used and the safe system of work for persons working on or near open or leading edges.

Electricity

Explain the site or company rules concerning:

- ☑ temporary or permanent repairs by competent persons on site
- ☑ use of 230 V equipment
- ☑ use of RCD or similar circuit breakers
- ☑ use of transformers and 110 V equipment
- ☑ testing, inspection and maintenance of portable electrical equipment (PAT testing).

Are there any other general rules regarding working with electricity?

Emergency procedure

Explain site or company procedures. What is the siren or alarm? Where are the emergency evacuation assembly points?

Explain the procedures to be followed in the event of an emergency other than fire. This may be civil disturbance, a bomb scare, structural collapse or other eventuality.

Environment

Environmental pollution can include the air, as well as the ground or water. Explain any specific issues of environmental protection and control concerning the company or site.

Escape routes

Explain the recognised escape routes on site and from buildings in the event of a fire or emergency.

Explain that access and egress routes must be well-defined and kept clear. How are they marked? How will they be lit when it is dark or during winter months? How will changes to the escape routes be notified as construction progresses?

Excavations

Explain the policy regarding:

- ☑ permit to dig systems
- ☑ excavation support and inspections
- ☑ proper entry and exit from an excavation, and edge protection around an excavation.

Eye protection

Explain if there are any specific eye protection issues, or rules applicable to the site or any particular work that is taking place. See also **personal protective equipment**.

Fall arrest

You may wish to comment on the use of safety nets, safety decking, air bags and other similar systems. See also **safety harnesses**.

Fall prevention

Explain the hierarchy of control measures that are to be used on site to prevent persons from falling or to catch them safely if they do fall. This will obviously vary depending on the type of site and work undertaken.

Fire

In the induction session you should at least cover the following:

- ☑ fire precautions, fire prevention and good housekeeping
- ☑ who will be responsible for summoning the emergency services
- ☑ location of:
  - – fire points
  - – fire extinguishers
- ☑ training and competence in the use of fire-fighting equipment
- ☑ testing of the fire alarm, fire drills and practice evacuations
- ☑ policy for hot works, including permits.

First aid

Clearly explain the arrangements for first aid provision.

- ☑ The location of the first-aid kit(s).
- ☑ The details of the first aider(s), emergency first aider(s) or appointed persons and how they can be identified and contacted in the event of an emergency.
- ☑ Location of the first-aid room.
- ☑ Emergency procedures that should be taken in the event of an injury.

Flammable liquids

If flammable liquids (such as paint thinners, solvents, spirit-based paints and others) are kept and used on site, explain the rules for:

- ☑ storage
- ☑ withdrawal from storage
- ☑ use and return to storage.

Health and safety committee

See also **consultation with employees.** If there is a site health and safety committee, explain the terms of reference for:

- ☑ the committee, membership and how often the committee meets
- ☑ agenda items and how the outcomes of meetings are made known to employees on site.

Hearing protection zones

See also **noise**. Are there any mandatory protection zones on site? How are they marked? Explain the supply and issue of hearing protectors and when they should be worn.

High-visibility clothing

Explain the site or company rules for when this clothing should be worn and clearly define the appropriate locations. Also clearly define the standard for high-visibility clothing.

Hoists

Explain the site or company rules for passenger hoists.

- ☑ Who is the competent person to operate the hoist?
- ☑ If any person can operate it, do they need training prior to being authorised as competent?
- ☑ If the controls are regarded as so simple that the hoist may almost be regarded as a public lift, is there any danger of controls being overridden?
- ☑ What is the maximum number of persons permitted in the hoist?
- ☑ Which rules apply regarding goods carried in the hoist?

Explain the site or company rules for goods hoists.

- ☑ Who is the authorised competent person to drive it or can any other persons be authorised?
- ☑ What are the rules for closing the gates and what is the safe working load?
- ☑ Explain that passengers cannot be carried.

Ladders/stepladders

Explain the company standards for:

- ☑ securing or tying ladders/stepladders
- ☑ use of ladders/stepladders for light work of short duration or gaining access
- ☑ any restrictions imposed on the use of ladders and stepladders (permits).

Lasers

If lasers are to be used on site, explain what class of laser is to be used and what, if any, hazards could be caused. Levelling lasers (used, for example, by suspended ceiling fixers) are not normally regarded as hazardous as long as appropriate health and safety rules are followed.

Legal issues

This is an opportunity to discuss any particular points of law that apply to the company or site where the induction training is being given. Explain that different projects and clients will have different rules and that employees should understand the need for each rule and how it will be enforced. Mention also the statutory health and safety law poster that must be displayed.

Lifting equipment

Explain the site or company rules for:

- ☑ who has the authority to use lifting equipment of varying sizes and types
- ☑ the duties of slingers and signallers
- ☑ testing and inspection of equipment, and current colour coding, if such a system is used.

Lighting

Explain the site or company rules for provision of work lighting and emergency lighting, including:

- ☑ the placing of luminaires
- ☑ extra lighting during winter months or for work outside normal hours.

Liquefied petroleum gas

Explain the rules for:

- ☑ use, storage and separation of full and empty cylinders
- ☑ separation from oxygen and acetylene, as appropriate
- ☑ use of hose check valves and flashback arresters
- ☑ use of fire extinguishers.

Manual handling

Explain the site or company rules for:

- ☑ the avoidance of manual handling wherever possible
- ☑ the use of mechanical devices to aid manual handling
- ☑ safe systems of work.

Method statements

Explain the importance of supervisors discussing with employees the method statement to be used for particular tasks, and the benefits to be gained from employee input into method statements.

Method statements must be specific to the site, task and persons carrying out the work.

Mobile elevating work platforms

Explain who has the competence to operate or use mobile elevating work platforms (MEWPs). Give the evidence required to prove competence and training. Where can MEWPs be used and under what ground conditions? Where are they not allowed? Explain the use of safety harnesses when working from platforms. Explain policy on emergency lowering and requirement to use anti-crush protection systems.

Near-miss incidents

Explain the importance of reporting all unsafe conditions and near misses and any site reporting scheme in operation. These can then be investigated and the appropriate remedial measures put into place so that the next near miss does not become an accident.

Needles and syringes

Employees should be warned to be very vigilant, particularly regarding the discovery of used hypodermic syringes (needles and risk of needlestick injury) and other drug-taking equipment.

Explain the action to be taken on finding discarded needles or receiving a needlestick injury.

It should be noted that most gloves in common use on site do not offer very much protection against a needlestick injury.

Noise

See also **hearing protection zones**. Explain the site or company rules concerning the use of equipment that produces excessive noise. Does the Local Authority impose any restrictions? Explain the use of hearing protection and noise control zones.

Occupational health

Stress the importance of employees reporting to supervisors any cases of ill health, as it may be potentially work-related. This is particularly important if employees are working where there may be rats, or if the area has been used for illegal drug taking and related paraphernalia may be found.

In the case of refurbishment and renovation works, there may be residual materials from previous occupants likely to cause ill health.

Construction dusts are the biggest cause of construction-related ill health, with over 5,000 people a year dying from respiratory diseases. Risk assessments and method statements must identify dust produced in any activity as a hazard, and control measures must be put in place to minimise exposure.

Overhead electricity cables

Explain the site or company rules on:

- ☑ location and marking
- ☑ allowable proximity for vehicles
- ☑ working nearby and precautions.

Permits to work

Explain company or site procedures regarding issuing, working with and the cancellation of permits to work. Where lock-off systems are used, explain the rules regarding padlock keys.

Personal protective equipment

Explain the site or company rules regarding:

- ☑ minimum personal protective equipment (PPE) (for example, safety helmets, safety footwear, high-visibility clothing, light eye protection and gloves)
- ☑ use of respiratory protection equipment (RPE) and other task specific PPE
- ☑ storage and maintenance of PPE (for example, light eye protection cleaning stations)
- ☑ any other issues (such as dress code).

Remind the inductees that PPE in general, and RPE in particular, should only be used as a means of last resort when all other control measures have been investigated and found to be impracticable. The need for PPE, apart from that which is mandatory, should be covered in the risk assessment and method statement.

Where task-specific PPE has been identified, the type or grade must be stated (for example, rather than just specifying 'dust mask' the type must be stated, such as FFP3-rated disposable dust mask).

Plant and equipment

Explain the site rules regarding:

- ☑ the authority to operate plant and equipment, including the requirement for competence cards, where necessary
- ☑ any type of plant/equipment that is prohibited (for example mains-powered hand tools)
- ☑ the need for noise control where appropriate
- ☑ the requirement for permits to work where appropriate.

Registration schemes

Explain the site or company rules regarding CSCS, CISRS, CPCS or other registration schemes.

Reporting defects

Explain the importance of reporting all defects in plant and equipment, scaffolding, supports for excavations, and so on. Early reporting will bring about swift remedial measures and help to prevent accidents. The possible consequences of not reporting defects may result in an accident or disciplinary procedures.

Restricted or prohibited areas

Explain whether there are any areas on site that are restricted to all people, or a specific class of people. Include what identifies a restricted area – typical examples are areas where demolition, impact cleaning, water jetting, or asbestos removal are taking place.

Risk assessments

Explain the significant findings of risk assessments, as they will affect staff on site as a whole, or those working on a particular activity. It may be useful to explain the risk assessment process and the health and safety benefits that can be gained by employees. See also **method statements**.

Safe systems of work

The crucial need arising out of risk assessments and method statements is for safe systems of work. Explain that site rules require employees to work in accordance with any safe systems of work that have been developed by the employer.

Safety harnesses

Explain the company or site requirements for inspecting, wearing, using and maintaining safety harnesses and lanyards.
See also **fall arrest**.

Safety policy

Explain any relevant areas of the company's health and safety policy, together with the organisation and arrangements for the implementation of the policy. If relevant, explain where a copy of the policy is displayed on site.

Safety signs and notices

Remind the audience that all employees must comply with all safety signs and notices at all times. Explain the whereabouts of any site noticeboard, hazard board and how changes and modifications to site rules will be made known to the workforce.

Scaffolding (including mobile scaffolds)

Explain the site rules regarding:

- ☑ who is allowed to erect, alter or dismantle tube and fitting or system-built scaffolds
- ☑ the implications (safety and disciplinary) of unauthorised dismantling or alteration of scaffolds
- ☑ assessing competency to erect proprietary aluminium or tower scaffolds
- ☑ the safe use of mobile tower scaffolds
- ☑ safe access/egress to and from scaffolds.

Explain any other company or site-specific rules about the use of scaffolding as either a working place, or as access to the working place.

Site layout

Explain whether any specific rules apply to pedestrian and traffic movement. This will depend on the size and complexity of the site. You may also include where contractors may lay down materials and which areas they may use for the prefabrication of components.

Site security

Security is very much allied to health and safety in that a breach of security can lead to trespassers on site and possible exposure to a risk of injury. Open a discussion if you have any particular company or on-site rules concerning security. Also consider the issue of health and safety awareness of site security staff, whether they are employees or a sub-contracted security company.

Skin protection

It may be appropriate to discuss the need for skin protection, both in terms of gloves and barrier creams. If barrier creams are used, where are they dispensed? Also explain that the types of gloves used must be the most suitable for the levels of protection needed. If it is likely to be a significant hazard, you should also include details of the risk of skin cancer associated with excessive exposure to the sun.

Smoking

Explain the policy on smoking in the workplace and the canteen, clearly identifying those areas where smoking is not allowed.

Tidiness (housekeeping)

Explain the importance of maintaining a tidy site in order to eliminate many of the slip, trip and fall hazards. Include:

- ☑ materials storage and delivery arrangements
- ☑ how materials are to be distributed and returned
- ☑ how and when to remove rubbish and excess materials
- ☑ who is responsible for organising the delivery of and removal of skips
- ☑ good housekeeping, sweeping up/vacuuming/dust extraction (general tidiness)
- ☑ maintaining tidy workplaces, access routes, staircases.

Toilets

See also **welfare facilities**. Explain the site or company rules regarding cleanliness, abuse of facilities and graffiti, and how such behaviour will be dealt with. Include the reporting of defects.

Traffic routes

These are dependent on the size and complexity of the site. Explain:

- ☑ one-way systems and the need to minimise or avoid reversing
- ☑ signallers or bankspersons
- ☑ segregation of pedestrians from vehicles and machines (pedestrian walkways).

Training

What training will be given to persons on site? Explain the need for all contractors to ensure that persons working for them on site have been trained and are competent to carry out the work they are required to do.

Underground services

Explain site or company procedures that should be followed if gas, electricity, telecommunications, fibre optics, water, sewerage and other underground services are discovered on site.

Vehicles

Explain the site rules for the presence and operation of vehicles on site. Include:

- ☑ the parking of private vehicles
- ☑ delivery vehicles (for example, constraints on access, delivery times, site restrictions, off-loading methods (for example, tower crane or telehandler), use of hi-abs and prevention of falls from vehicles)
- ☑ keeping clear of site (working) vehicles
- ☑ who is allowed to operate plant on site, and provide proof of competence to operate plant
- ☑ the security of vehicle keys when not in use
- ☑ security measures to make vehicles unavailable to trespassers and children during non-working hours
- ☑ traffic routes, speed limits and noise (for example, time limitations imposed by the Local Authority).

Vibration

Many people are still unaware of the problems that can be caused by high-speed rotary and percussive equipment. Explain the potential severity of vibration white finger and the company or site policy regarding:

- ☑ the use of vibrating equipment and maximum trigger use times
- ☑ the limitations of PPE
- ☑ design and selection of tools and equipment
- ☑ rest breaks and the rotation of work
- ☑ the symptoms of vibration white finger
- ☑ the need for employees to seek medical advice if they have any symptoms.

Waste disposal

Describe the location of skips and other waste containers. Explain the segregation of waste. Who is responsible for the removal of waste from the workplace? Explain the company or site policy if contractors do not clear away their own waste.

Waste minimisation

Explain that this is a financial issue as well as an environmental matter. It is also closely linked with site tidiness, pollution control, housekeeping and accident prevention. Effective waste minimisation is also an issue within sustainable construction and there are company and national benefits to be gained. There is more likelihood of a project being completed on time and to budget if waste is minimised. See also **environment**.

Welfare facilities

Explain:

- ☑ the location of the welfare facilities and, if appropriate, the opening hours of site canteens
- ☑ responsibilities for the cleaning and maintenance of the facilities
- ☑ the provision of barrier creams and rehydrating lotions
- ☑ the need for good personal hygiene.

Working at height

This is allied to fall prevention, safe systems of work and PPE. Explain the company or site rules for:

- ☑ working at height, including safe systems of work
- ☑ competence of employees
- ☑ protection of those below, including the public
- ☑ the prevention of materials falling (use of containment and debris nets).

Working near, on or over water

Explain the site or company rules for working near, on or over water, including:

- ☑ the wearing of life jackets, life preservers or flotation devices
- ☑ prevention of falls into water
- ☑ the rescue of anyone who has fallen into water, plus lookouts and alarms.

Appendix B – Employer responsibilities

The following information is provided as an aide-memoire to training providers, for any questions that may arise during or after an induction training programme.

Set out below, in an abbreviated form, are the principal responsibilities of employers, managers and supervisors. For ease of presentation, the reader is assumed to be an employer.

- ☑ Ensure, so far as is reasonably practicable, the health, safety and welfare of employees.
- ☑ Display an employer's liability compulsory insurance certificate.
- ☑ Have a general statement of health and safety policy.
- ☑ Prepare and display a written health and safety policy, if you employ five or more persons.
- ☑ Make employees aware of your company health and safety policy.
- ☑ Display an approved poster or give each employee a copy of an approved leaflet to comply with the Health and Safety (Information for Employees) Regulations.
- ☑ Carry out risk assessments of your work and record the significant findings, if you employ five or more persons.
- ☑ Implement any control measures identified by your risk assessment.
- ☑ Regularly review risk assessments and any associated control measures.
- ☑ Ensure that scaffolding is only erected, altered or dismantled under the supervision of a competent person.
- ☑ Appoint a competent person to assist the company with health and safety requirements, where necessary.
- ☑ Establish a safety committee, if requested by two union-appointed safety representatives.
- ☑ Assess manual handling operations in the workplace and take appropriate steps to reduce the risk of injury to employees.
- ☑ Ensure all accidents that result in injury, however slight, are entered in the accident book and investigated.
- ☑ Report to the HSE all reportable accidents, dangerous occurrences and notifiable diseases.
- ☑ Provide employees with PPE, as necessary.
- ☑ Avoid entry into confined spaces, wherever possible.
- ☑ Protect employees who may be exposed to asbestos at work.
- ☑ Ensure that all excavations are safe and that work in excavations is carried out safely.
- ☑ Provide sufficient and suitable welfare facilities on construction sites, including sanitary conveniences, washing facilities, drinking water and changing facilities.
- ☑ Provide information, instruction, training and supervision to ensure the health and safety of all employees.
- ☑ Appoint trained and competent persons for the purpose of mounting abrasive wheels.
- ☑ Examine, test and properly maintain plant, equipment, cranes, lifting appliances and associated working gear at regular intervals, and record the findings.
- ☑ Provide adequate first-aid facilities with sufficiently trained first aiders and appointed persons.
- ☑ Consult with your employees on health and safety matters.
- ☑ Ask only competent persons to carry out work on electrical installations and appliances.
- ☑ Take measures to prevent or adequately control employees' exposure to harmful dusts and fumes.
- ☑ Prepare and maintain a construction phase plan appropriate to your operations.
- ☑ Ensure that the workplace is safe and without risk to the health of employees.
- ☑ Take the necessary steps to ensure that the health and safety of the public is not put at risk by works being carried out.

Appendix C – Employee responsibilities

Below, in an abbreviated form, are the main responsibilities of employees. The reader is assumed to be an employee.

- ☑ Co-operate with your employer and follow any information, instructions and training given to you.
- ☑ Do not interfere with or misuse anything your employer has provided in the interests of health, safety and welfare.
- ☑ Take reasonable care at all times and make sure that you do not endanger yourself or any other person.
- ☑ Use all tools and equipment safely and in accordance with instructions given or training received.
- ☑ Report any defects or potential hazards in equipment to your supervisor as soon as possible.
- ☑ Make proper use of any safe system of work or mechanical means provided by your employer in connection with manual handling.
- ☑ Only operate the plant and equipment you have been trained and authorised to use.
- ☑ Use the PPE supplied by your employer correctly, take care of it and report any loss or defects in the equipment.
- ☑ Report to your employer any work situation that might present a danger.
- ☑ Do not erect, alter or dismantle scaffolding unless competent to do so or under the supervision of a competent person.
- ☑ When operating goods hoists, keep the gates closed except when loading. Do not override any controls. Do not allow any passengers.
- ☑ Use only the proper safe means provided for entering and leaving an excavation.
- ☑ Do not block or obstruct any access or means of escape route.
- ☑ Make full use of any control measures provided to prevent or limit exposure to substances hazardous to health, and wear the PPE provided.
- ☑ Observe safe use and handling instructions for hazardous substances, and return unused quantities to the designated store.
- ☑ Do not use a MEWP for any use other than as a work platform.
- ☑ Co-operate with health and safety inspectors, as required.
- ☑ Do not remove safety guards or stop any safety device fitted to any plant or equipment from working.
- ☑ Do not ride on plant or vehicles in unauthorised and insecure places.
- ☑ Recognise the importance of personal cleanliness, especially when working with substances harmful to the skin.
- ☑ Never exceed the safe working load of any equipment.
- ☑ Report to your supervisor all accidents that cause any injury to you.
- ☑ Understand and comply with all signs that are displayed.
- ☑ Wear ear protectors in designated areas where mandatory warning signs are displayed.
- ☑ Follow all company and site health and safety rules.

07

Communication with non-English speaking workers

Contents

Overview

Good communication is essential for the management of health and safety on construction sites.

Communication problems can occur where workers have limited or no understanding of English, particularly during site induction.

This chapter offers advice to those who may not have company communication policies, and offers some suggested approaches.

7.1 Introduction

The number of workers on UK sites, where English is not their first language, has increased over recent years.

Some of these workers have excellent skills in spoken and written English, but there are others for whom understanding English is a problem. This can be a barrier to effective communication of health and safety information. However, failure to engage with non-English speaking workers for this reason will almost certainly be in breach of the provisions of race relations legislation.

7.2 Important points

- ☑ Employers are legally required to provide information that is comprehensible, in other words provided in a format that can be understood by the worker.
- ☑ This requirement can result in problems where the recipients of the information have limited or no understanding of English, particularly during site induction.
- ☑ Communicating using images has the potential to overcome these problems, regardless of the mix of languages spoken on site.
- ☑ A bank of images, each representing a hazard or a simple instruction has been developed.
- ☑ These images have been developed by CITB into a useful, colour coded resource for use on site, *Safety critical communication – Toolbox talks* (GT 701).
- ☑ It is likely that it will be necessary to hold separate training sessions to assess the understanding of safety critical words and phrases by those with English language problems.
- ☑ Confirming that the workers being assessed can associate each image with a spoken short phrase in plain English will give supervisors and managers confidence that the workers have an understanding of safety critical words in English.
- ☑ Due to their simplicity, these phrases aid translation into other languages, if needed.
- ☑ Before using any images, workers' competence, training and language skills must be assessed. This will also indicate the level of supervision required generally.
- ☑ The images can be used to support site inductions, toolbox talks or other training, or superimposed on site plans to identify the location of welfare facilities, fire-fighting equipment, and so on.
- ☑ The images also help to fill gaps in translation, as well as improving memory recall of site rules.
- ☑ If appropriate, the images can enhance and complement existing procedures (for example using interpreters), rather than replace them.
- ☑ An understanding of the images should not be solely relied upon to ensure that work of a higher risk nature can be carried out safely.

7.3 Managing the language situation

Contractors who employ workers who cannot speak and/or understand English have a few options when deciding how to manage communications. These include hiring a bilingual supervisor who can give information, instruction and training to workers.

Alternatively, English speaking co-workers are often used on site to communicate with non-English speaking workers. However, their competence (both technically in construction and as a translator) must be assessed first.

Another option is for training materials to be translated or to be represented in a pictorial form (images) *(refer to 7.5)*. The effectiveness of images to overcome language barriers has been confirmed through research.

The images were developed from British Standard safety signs, Health and Safety Executive (HSE) guidance documents and other picture-based guidance. These images were tested for comprehension on live sites with foreign workers and refined to help contractors to carry out effective health and safety training and, in so doing, discharge their legal duties.

The black and white images were developed for a generic site induction and targeted at the most critical health, safety and welfare issues relevant to construction workers. However, these are only examples of a larger database of images. The coloured images and the text *(refer to 7.6)* demonstrate the principles of using the CITB visual communication resource *Safety critical communication – Toolbox talks* (GT 701).

For a full contents list of GT 701 refer to Appendix A.

7.4 Pre-start assessments

Before any worker starts on site the following facts must be established.

- ☑ The worker's competence and training.
- ☑ The worker's understanding of English.
- ☑ Supervision required.

The type of work to be done by the worker will dictate the required level of competence and identify any training needed. Regardless of language issues foreign workers must meet the level of competence and training expected of **any** worker asked to do the task(s). Therefore, contractors should apply the same criteria for non/low-English speaking workers as they do for English speakers, which will require some form of competency assessment.

It is possible that some foreign workers will have trade qualifications gained in their home countries.

www.

The National Academic Recognition Information Centre for the UK (NARIC) is a Government-funded agency that offers a service to compare overseas qualifications with UK ones. Although not comprehensive, it is a useful resource.

With regard to training undertaken in the United Kingdom, holding a CSCS, CPCS or similar card will indicate that an acceptable level of training has been undertaken and a minimum level of health and safety knowledge is held.

Failure to prove an acceptable level of competence will indicate that further training is required before considering the other pre-start factors. Such training is beyond the scope of this chapter.

Assuming that the worker meets the contractor's competence criteria, the next thing to consider is the worker's language skills. NARIC can also provide assistance in this respect. There are a number of methods for assessing a worker's English language skills, which use simple self-assessment criteria.

One of these is the Association of Language Testers in Europe (ALTE) 'can do' statements. These can be objectively described and assessed by non-specialists. Therefore, a worker's language skills can be easily determined by site managers and supervisors by following the guidance provided in the ALTE work statements summary *(see table below and on the next page)*.

Workers below ALTE breakthrough level are those with no English language skills whatsoever, who need an interpreter or written translation for all communications. Furthermore, it may be unwise to assume these workers can read in their own language.

To prove their competence these workers will have to demonstrate their understanding of the images without the benefit of reference to the phrases.

Most workers who have lived and worked in the UK for at least one year may have picked up a basic level of understanding of English at listening breakthrough level or Level 1. Workers at this level will find the images and phrases to be useful learning aids.

Co-workers, who can interpret for their colleagues, will need to be at least ALTE Level 3 for listening and speaking. The presence of an interpreter does not make the images redundant as they can still fill gaps that may be lost in translation.

The combination of competence, training and language skills will dictate the level of supervision required. Another factor, as with any worker, will be the result of the employer's risk assessment for the task(s).

However, where there is a language barrier to communication, the level of supervision will also have to consider an appropriate ratio of workers to each bilingual supervisor. This can vary from as much as 1:20 to 1:1 depending on the circumstances.

Where workers are grouped close together in the same area and undertaking low risk work the ratio can be high. But, if the workers are dispersed around the site and/or undertaking higher risk work, the ratio may need to be as low as 1:1.

Lone working for workers with non/low-English language skills is not recommended.

ALTE work statements summary table

ALTE level	Listening or speaking	Reading	Writing
ALTE breakthrough level	CAN take and pass on simple messages of a routine kind, such as 'Friday meeting 10 a.m.'.	CAN understand short reports or product descriptions on familiar matters, if these are expressed in simple language and the contents are predictable.	CAN write a simple routine request to a colleague, such as 'Can I have 20X please?'
ALTE Level 1	CAN state simple requirements within own job area, such as 'I want to order 25 of...'.	CAN understand most short reports or manuals of a predictable nature within their own area of expertise, provided enough time is given.	CAN write a short, comprehensible note of request to a colleague or a known contact in another company.
ALTE Level 2	CAN offer advice to clients within own job area on simple matters.	CAN understand the general meaning of non-routine letters and theoretical articles within own work area.	CAN make reasonably accurate notes at a meeting or seminar where the subject matter is familiar and predictable.

ALTE work statements summary table			
ALTE level	**Listening or speaking**	**Reading**	**Writing**
ALTE Level 3	CAN take and pass on most messages that are likely to require attention during a normal working day.	CAN understand most correspondence, reports and factual product literature they are likely to come across.	CAN deal with all routine requests for goods or services.
ALTE Level 4	CAN contribute effectively to meetings and seminars within own area of work and argue for or against a case.	CAN understand correspondence expressed in non-standard language.	CAN handle a wide range of routine and non-routine situations in which professional services are requested from colleagues or external contacts.
ALTE Level 5	CAN advise on/handle complex, delicate or contentious issues, such as legal or financial matters, to the extent that they have the necessary specialist knowledge.	CAN understand reports and articles likely to be encountered during their work, including complex ideas expressed in complex language.	CAN make full and accurate notes and continue to participate in a meeting or seminar.

(Reproduced with permission from ALTE.)

For further information on the ALTE Can Do project refer to the ALTE website.

7.5 Critical health, safety and welfare images

The critical health, safety and welfare images that have been designed to enhance induction and other training are available on the companion website.

Each image is set out in a similar format, as shown below.

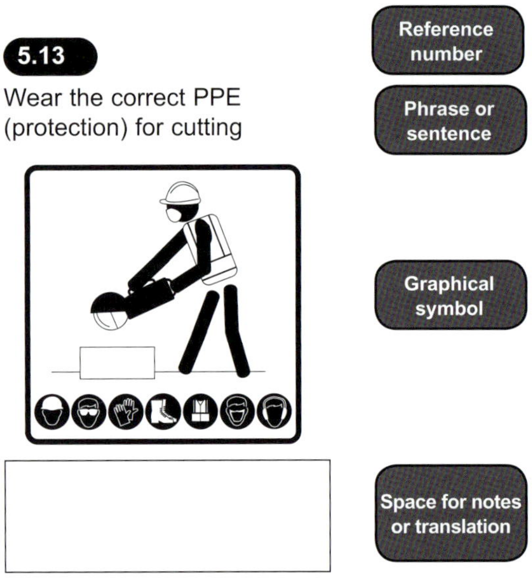

The **reference number** at the top of each image is for ease of identification.

The next element is a **short phrase or sentence.** These have been developed, with help from language experts, to:

- communicate, in plain English, the particular health and safety issue depicted by the graphical symbol
- aid translation into other languages.

The phrase or sentence will remind the person delivering the training of the response required from the person being assessed during the induction. Depending upon the circumstances, a decision will have to be made as to whether it is more beneficial to reveal or hide the phrase or sentence during the assessment. Having sight of the phrase or sentence may have the potential to help workers with a limited understanding of written English to associate the written words with the message of the graphical symbol.

The **graphical symbol** is the main element in each image. Most are self-explanatory. Some enable the person delivering the training to add site-specific information (for example the postal address of the site (image 2.1) or site telephone number (image 2.2)).

As demonstrated in the figures below, it is recommended that some of the images are regarded as linked and are shown sequentially to convey the correct meaning:

3.6

Do not leave the gate open

3.7

Keep the gate locked

If image 3.7 is shown to a worker who cannot understand the written phrase, it could be misinterpreted as 'the site is closed' or 'keep out'. However, by showing image 3.6 and 3.7 in sequence, a visual link is created and the chance of misinterpretation is reduced.

7.6 Delivering a safety critical communication toolbox talk

1. Find the hazard in the contents list.
2. Turn to the appropriate page (yellow image).
3. View the risk to health or safety on the opposing red page.

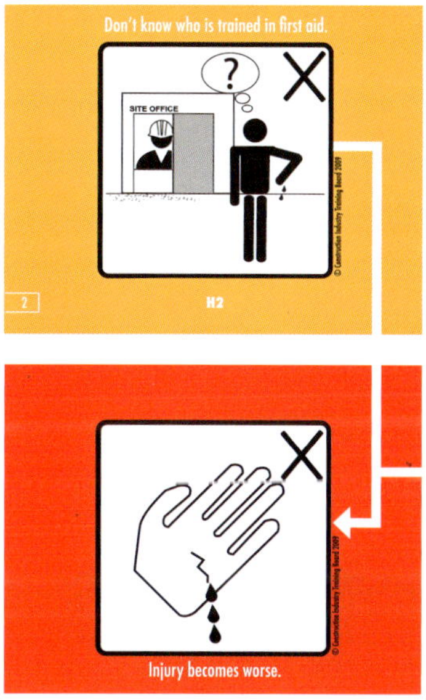

4. Fold out the red page to reveal the necessary control measures on the green page(s).
5. Deliver the toolbox talk.

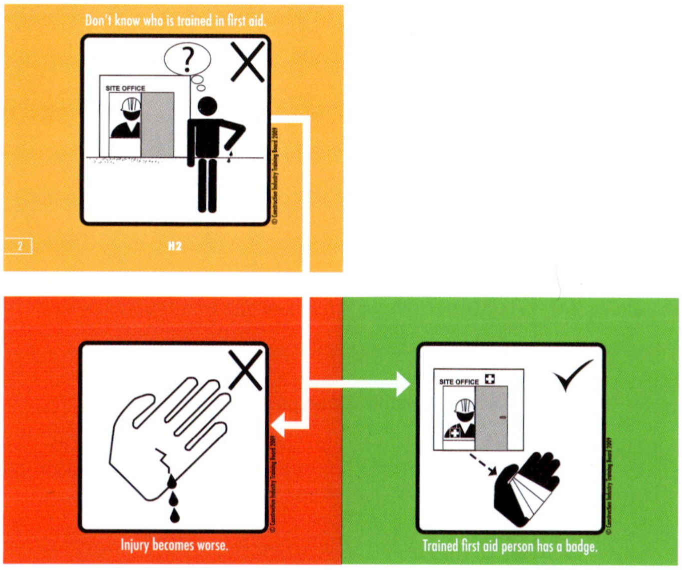

7.6.1 Explanation of the elements on each coloured page

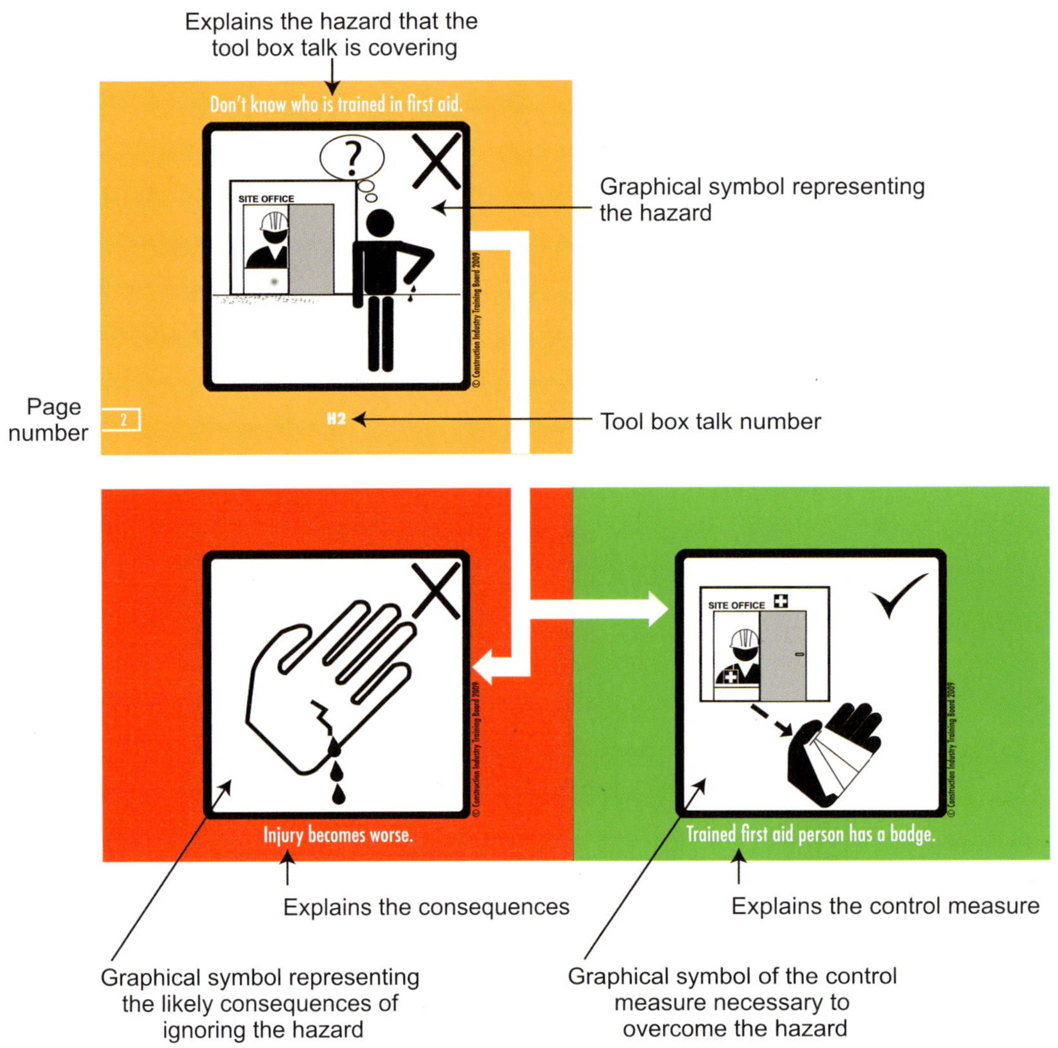

7.7 Using the images

7.7.1 Safety critical communication – Toolbox talks

The method of using the colour images contained in the CITB publication *Safety critical communication – Toolbox talks* (GT 701) is outlined earlier in this chapter *(refer to 7.6)*.

For further details and to obtain GT 701 refer to the CITB website.

7.7.2 Site induction

The critical health, safety and welfare images are examples of a wider resource for use by site managers or supervisors. It is envisaged that the primary use will be during the induction training of foreign workers.

They can also be used to support other forms of training (such as during the delivery of toolbox talks to foreign workers). However, they have their limitations as described later.

The images are intended to enhance the induction procedures for non/low-English speaking workers. However, in future it may be possible to import the images directly into existing induction presentations.

With careful forethought, this may enable foreign workers to be successfully inducted during the same presentation as other workers. If this approach is taken it is likely that additional effort will be required to confirm the retained level of understanding of the foreign workers, possibly including subsequent follow-up checks.

Existing induction training procedures for foreign workers who do not understand English may involve the use of an interpreter. However, problems can occur during translation and the use of the images may help to fill any gaps in worker understanding.

7.7.3 Site plans

Some of the images (such as those showing the location of welfare facilities, fire-fighting equipment and assembly points) lend themselves to being overlaid (physically or electronically) on site layout plans.

Depending on the size of the plans, it may be feasible in the future for copies of the images to be electronically superimposed directly onto the plans in the appropriate location, or placed in the margin with arrows pointing to the actual location. These can be displayed during site inductions and left in a suitable place for future reference.

7.7.4 Site inspections

The images can be used during site walkabout. For example, a worker not wearing essential personal protective equipment (PPE) can be informed using images starting with the number '5', which show items of PPE required on construction sites.

Furthermore, the images in the CITB database are presented in the sequence Hazard-Risk-Control(s) and can be used to educate the worker by showing them a hazard, which may be an unsafe act or condition, followed by the potential risk (consequences) and the necessary control(s).

Management controls are beyond the worker's direct authority but dealt with using an image containing a 'report to supervisor' message.

Workers can be tested for comprehension by asking them to consider whether an image is good or bad practice; or by showing the first sequence of images (hazard/risk) and asking the worker to identify the correct control image.

In addition, observation of workers after instruction has been given will confirm whether they have implemented the necessary controls/safe system of work.

7.7.5 Limitations of using pictorial images

Whilst pictorial images are very useful aids for communicating health and safety information, they have their limitations. For example, some of the critical health, safety and welfare images contain some work that needs a permit to work. However, the rationale for introducing a particular type of permit or the procedures for obtaining one must be taught through detailed instruction, not easily covered solely by pictorial images.

Images should not be seen as a complete alternative to using interpreters but rather as tools to enhance existing practices; the law requires this should include interpreters where appropriate.

Appendix A – Safety critical communication – Toolbox talks (GT 701) – Full content list

Volume 1

Occupational health and hygiene

First aid

H1 – First-aid equipment

H2 – First-aid person

Health on site

H3 – Dirty toilets

H4 – Dirty skin

H59 – Dust

H68 – Noise

H78 – Hours of work

H79 – Rats and mice

H80 – Alcohol

H81 – Illegal drugs

H82 – Exposure to the sun

H83 – Hand-arm vibration

Manual handling

H5 – Lifting (1)

H8 – Lifting (2)

H9 – Lifting (3)

Working at height

Ladders

H12 – Broken ladder (1)

H13 – Broken ladder (2)

H14 – Ladder positioning (1)

H15 – Ladder positioning (2)

H16 – Ladder positioning (3)

H19 – Ladder positioning (4)

H17 – Ladder use (1)

H18 – Ladder use (2)

H21 – Use of stepladder

H29 – Ladder use (3)

H55 – Ladders not in use

H75 – Ladder use, handholds (4)

H76 – Ladder use, uneven surface (5)

H77 – Ladder use, weak surface (6)

Working platforms/hoists

H20 – Safe working load (platform)

H22 – Safe working load (hoist)

H23 – Competent use

H24 – Guard-rail

Mobile work platforms (MWP)

H25 – Use of MWP (1)

H26 – Use of MWP (2)

H27 – Use of MWP (3)

H28 – Use of MWP (4)

Volume 2

Scaffolding

H30 – Use of scaffolding (1)

H31 – Use of scaffolding (2)

H32 – Use of scaffolding (3)

H33 – Incomplete scaffolding

H74 – Position of people below

Working on a roof

H34 – No edge protection

H35 – Fragile roof

Plant and equipment, safe use

Hand tools

H41 – Use of abrasive (cutting) wheel

H42 – Use of cartridge tool (nail gun)

H43 – Electric tools, condition of (1)

H44 – Electric tools, condition of (2)

H45 – Electric tools, correct voltage

H56 – Use of hand tools near electricity

H67 – Hidden services

Mobile elevating work platforms (MEWP)

H37 – Use of MEWP (1)

H38 – Use of MEWP (2)

H39 – Safe working loads

H40 – MEWP and people

Mobile cranes/equipment

H46 – Mobile crane, correct use of

H47 – Mobile equipment and passengers

H48 – Mobile equipment and people

H49 – Mobile equipment and untrained personnel

H50 – Mobile equipment, left unattended

H60 – Excavator near electricity

Vehicles

H51 – Vehicle reversing

H52 – Unsafe loads

Excavations

H36 – Excavation unprotected

H57 – Moving equipment into excavation

H58 – Alighting from excavation

H61 – Excavation unprotected

H62 – Incorrect excavation

H63 – Mobile plant near excavation

H64 – Excavation with no support

H65 – Excavation internal supports removed

H66 – Excavation with no support

Fire and flammable substances

H69 – Fire hazards – source of fuel

H70 – Fire hazards – use of flammable substances

H71 – Fire extinguishers

H72 – Smoking

H73 – Correct positioning of gas cylinders

Other hazards at work

H6 – Blocking hazard (1)

H10 – Blocking hazard (2)

H7 – Bad light

H11 – Housekeeping

H53 – Hazardous substances, storage

H54 – Security of site

A
07

08

Behavioural safety

Contents

Supporting information

G: Checklists and forms

GT 700 Toolbox talks

Overview

The chapter explores what behavioural safety is and the elements of working practice that can have an impact on this, both positively and negatively. It offers information and models that can inform good practice in this significant area of focus for health and safety.

Studies have shown that up to 90% of accidents are attributable in some extent to human failures. Human factors are understandably an important focus for many accident investigations. The importance and relevance of these to preventing incidents, injuries, deaths and ill health within the workplace, as identified through case study research, therefore warrant the attention of all organisations, managers and employees.

8.1 Introduction

Promoting safe behaviour at work is a crucial part of the management of health and safety, because behaviour defines the real experience of systems and procedures. Having good systems in place does not on its own ensure successful health and safety management. The level of success is defined by how organisations 'live' their systems on a day-to-day basis – the behavioural culture of the organisation.

The Health and Safety Executive (HSE) identifies behavioural safety as one important area within the overarching title of human factors that:

> **refer to environmental, organisational and job factors, and human and individual characteristics, which influence behaviour at work in a way which can affect health and safety.**

Behavioural safety provides a focus for understanding and influencing the way managers and individuals act the way they do in relation to work and decision making. It is based on the following process.

Asking the workforce for input and ideas

- ☑ Identifying and making evident safe and unsafe practice.
- ☑ Observing and intervening, where appropriate, to encourage safe or amend unsafe practice.
- ☑ Feeding back of vital information to inform decision making.
- ☑ Training, process, material and environmental change, as appropriate.
- ☑ Recognising safe working practices and supporting good practices.

Behavioural safety represents a proactive rather than a reactive process, engaging all managers and workers within a culture of continuous improvement and safety awareness. For this reason, communication at and across all levels of an organisation is a vital strand to the development of a successful and influential strategy.

> **Useful HSE publications are available from the HSE website.**

> **The HSE has identified human and organisational behaviours to be significant factors in relation to workplace accidents and time lost to work. Studies have shown that up to 90% of accidents are attributable in some extent to human failure.**

Raising the awareness of managers, supervisors and workers to ensure that effective behavioural safety change is an expected part of the working culture will be a significant factor in helping to reduce these numbers.

8.2 Important points

- ☑ Historically improvements in health and safety standards have been achieved through **engineering technology/controls** (plant and equipment) and **safety management systems** (risk assessments, permits to work and so on).
- ☑ These improvements will not fully eradicate incidents and accidents.
- ☑ By understanding how people make decisions and **why people act** as a consequence is the vital third element.
- ☑ The biggest gain in improving health and safety performance is integrating and understanding the human element of risk management.

- Companies that incorporate behavioural safety programmes into the day-to-day running of their business see dramatic drops in accident rates.
- In order for a behavioural safety approach to work, consistently high standards of engineering technology/controls and safety management systems need to be established.
- Behavioural safety is not a quick-win initiative – it takes time and commitment from all levels of a company or organisation. It is not an alternative to applying sound, basic principles of health and safety management.
- Effective leadership, management and workforce support is crucial for the success of any programme.
- People may generally think they are working safely, or that the risk of something happening is minimal due to their knowledge and past experience. Those observing can often see that the risk is greater than first thought and thus intervention techniques play an important role in developing a positive safety culture.
- Workers respond more positively to co-worker/peer intervention.
- Worker engagement is a fundamental component of any behavioural safety programme.

8.3 Why use a behavioural safety approach?

Over recent years, significant improvements have been achieved in health, safety and environmental performance. This has been gained largely through technological advances and improved focus through the use of management systems.

Commitment by the team is vital

A levelling-off of this successful downward trend has led to an increased focus on the human elements associated with health and safety practices, awareness, commitment and decision-making.

It is believed that a behavioural safety approach by all associated with the construction and other industries will contribute to more improvements over time.

Evidence and support for this has come from HSE case study investigations and research into major reportable accidents.

The case studies identify actions and strategies that have been implemented within the example organisations in order to improve specific health and safety practice.

From this work, the HSE and contributing partners have identified a list of human factor issues. These include separate notes on the following.

- Introducing human factors.
- Competence.
- Humans and risk (integration of human factors into risk assessments and accident investigation).
- Written procedures.
- Emergency response.
- Maintenance.
- Safety culture.
- Safety critical communications.
- Alarm handling and control room design.
- Fatigue.
- Organisational change and transition management.
- Human factors and the major accident prevention policy (MAPP).

The HSE also notes other problems (such as those listed below) found from inspection and assessment.

- Too much emphasis being placed on reducing personal accidents (slips, trips, falls), without an equal focus on preventing major accidents.
- Failing to realise that safety culture is about everyone in the company, including managers, not just the frontline staff.
- Not being clear about how the safety management system will prevent or reduce human errors, which may lead to major accidents.

To be effective, a behaviour-based approach to health and safety requires the following.

- Clear and unambiguous leadership from the top down.
- Management commitment to the culture of behavioural safety.
- Buy-in at all levels to making the scheme work.
- An up-front commitment in terms of time, effort and determination.
- Scheme sponsors who believe in the value of making it work, who can be sympathetic to the reasons why some people behave in an unsafe manner and persuasive in convincing those people that they should not behave in that way.
- Effective communication of the scheme objectives.
- A concerted effort to convince those affected that they will not be disadvantaged by the changes that will come about as a result of introducing the approach.
- Effective engagement of everyone involved in the approach; not just those working on site but people involved in decision making too.

www.

The HSE has produced a human factors checklist, which is available on its website.

The checklist *(which can also be found in Section G: Checklists and forms)* offers a series of self-assessment statements that may provide a useful benchmark for areas involved in the human factors approach to behavioural safety.

8.4 Preparing to implement a behavioural approach

The HSE's core guidance defines human factors as the interaction between three main areas affecting human performance at work.

- The job.
- The individual.
- The organisation.

A 08

8.4.1 The job

The job will ideally be well designed to match the skills and strengths of the individual or team undertaking it. In this way, the job is matched to the human.

Job design will have a focus on the following.

- Areas of work and the environment in which it is carried out.
- Materials and tools.
- Control and display panels and devices.
- Communication and management systems.
- All job-related written guidance and information.

8.4.2 The individual

The organisation and managers will also select individuals who are well matched to meet the needs of the job (fitting the human to the job). Individuals should have:

- the most suitable physique (size, build and strength)
- the right personality
- aptitude
- competence (the right skills, understanding, experience and training).

8.4.3 The organisation

The organisation will ensure that it supports managers to:

- take responsibility for all aspects of work and work design
- devise and maintain a good safety management system
- encourage a good safety culture by showing genuine commitment
- consult the workforce on important decisions
- commit to learning from the latest thinking on good practice in safety
- openly encourage identification and shared learning from accidents and near misses.

Together, these three areas constitute the solid foundations on which behavioural safety programmes can be addressed and developed.

!

Good practice and case studies indicate that prior to commencing any behavioural safety change programme, intervention, factors relating to the job, the individual and the organisation will all need to be considered.

Before sites embark on a behavioural safety programme, it is recommended that the following preparation has taken place.

- ☑ All hazards have been identified.
- ☑ Human performance issues have been identified and managed (particularly in relation to safety critical roles and activities).
- ☑ The hierarchy of control has been applied to prevent the occurrence of identified hazards, or minimise their consequences should they occur.
- ☑ The site has the required engineering, operating and maintenance capability and experience (including appropriate staffing levels).
- ☑ Accurate operating procedures are available for all eventualities, including emergencies.
- ☑ Individuals (operators) are fully prepared to deal with all conditions. This will include identification of training needs, training, assessment, rehearsal and reassessment.
- ☑ Training should include underlying knowledge of the process, so that operators can troubleshoot (identify and respond to abnormal situations as they develop). It should not just provide the minimum knowledge required to operate the plant. This will help to manage residual risk arising from hazards that were not identified or effectively addressed.
- ☑ Lessons have been learnt from site, company and industry experience.
- ☑ Succession planning ensures that corporate knowledge is retained.
- ☑ Safety management arrangements and risk control measures have been reviewed to ensure that they remain usable and relevant.

It is recommended that only when these technical and systems issues have been addressed can the timing and appropriateness of a behavioural programme be addressed.

Unsafe working – reasons for implementing a behavioural safety approach

The guidance also goes on to highlight the following for consideration.

- ☑ Do not underestimate the resources required – it is not a one-off exercise, but a new way of working that must be maintained for any positive results to be sustained.
- ☑ Do not be over-optimistic – not all interventions are completely successful in their main aim. High expectations may lead to later disillusionment.
- ☑ Be clear about what you want to achieve and how you will know that you have achieved it.
- ☑ Pilot the intervention (for example, to ensure that the approach is workable, that the facilitators or observers understand what is required and that the appropriate data is being recorded).
- ☑ Talk to similar companies and trade associations about their interventions and experiences.
- ☑ As with all interventions, listen to your employees and use the process to improve dialogue – involve employees early in the choice of programme.
- ☑ Make the language and style of the package your own, as off-the-shelf packages may not be appropriate for your site's needs.
- ☑ Use strong site facilitators – the success of such interventions is greatly helped by using a personable, experienced and respected site personnel as facilitators.
- ☑ Ensure that the focus is on the root causes of behaviours.
- ☑ On major hazard sites, don't neglect process safety (beware 'what gets measured gets done').

8.5 Factors influencing a behavioural approach

The practicalities involved in successfully implementing a behavioural approach to health and safety are listed below.

- ☑ Preparation (see above) – knowing what you are doing and why.
- ☑ Establishing an effective system of two-way communication to develop mutual trust between the management and workforce.
- ☑ Engaging the right people in the decision making.
- ☑ Observing people at work.
- ☑ Assessing their safe and unsafe behaviours (being non-judgemental).
- ☑ Making timely and appropriate interventions.
- ☑ Establishing why unsafe behaviours take place.
- ☑ Influencing those who behave unsafely not to do so in the future.
- ☑ Recognising safe behaviours and, if appropriate, rewarding them.
- ☑ Continuing assessment and research whilst looking for improvements in safe behaviour.

The overall and wider benefits to this implementation can include the following.

- ☑ More effective communication regarding safety between management and frontline workers.
- ☑ Greater management visibility and engagement.
- ☑ Increased efficiency.
- ☑ Greater flexibility and effectiveness of workers.
- ☑ A reduction in the number of workplace injuries.
- ☑ Improvement in the standards of health and safety.
- ☑ Reduced physical and financial losses for the individual and the employer.
- ☑ The extension of safe working practices into home life.

The following are all factors that are relevant and require consideration when implementing a behavioural safety programme.

8.5.1 Psychology of behaviour

Behavioural safety applies tried and tested psychological principles in order to mediate the way people and organisations do things, particularly how people act or behave in respect of their own health and safety and that of others.

Among many other factors, behavioural approach takes into account how people think, act, behave and respond to certain situations. It also considers how people's immediate surroundings can influence their thoughts and actions.

8.5.1.1 Thought processes

Contrary to previous belief, the conscious or alert state of mind can only be actively engaged in one activity or thought process at any one time.

Recent neuroscience research and findings have identified that distractions from a single task can, at best, result in less efficient working and at worst, can contribute to a stress response. This is particularly so if someone tries to finish a task but cannot as time goes on.

The human brain is strongly programmed to avoid a perceived threat and generally (but less strongly) programmed for reward from tasks achieved. This latter results in the small, so-called 'dopamine spike', which drives us to continue with our reward-based behaviour.

In practical terms, if a distraction disturbs a person's thought processes or task, they may, for example, trip over a toolbox they have placed on some steps or fall into a hole they have recently dug. Other thoughts have entered their conscious mind and the hazardous situation is momentarily forgotten.

At the most basic level, good workplace practice (such as avoiding distractions and removing hazards immediately) can support the wider behavioural safety programme.

Often the ability to increase safety awareness by the individual doing a mental risk assessment (that is, asking 'What is going to put me at risk while I do this job?') is not improved or encouraged once relevant training has been undertaken. Practising this type of self-awareness has safety benefits, especially if it is recorded.

People at work benefit from being able to discuss and take responsibility for the day-to-day aspects of their job and from feeling competent to do so. The human side of the working environment is a highly significant factor in determining the success of a behavioural safety environment and this warrants a focus on management training and commitment.

By helping people to understand the implications of how they work and engaging their knowledge, we can identify the process that integrates human factors into the core management system of the business. Effort should be targeted at encouraging positive, open and real communication that resolves issues when they arise, rather than keeping them hidden until an incident occurs.

8.5.1.2 Habitual behaviours

Habits are subconscious ways of thinking, both positive and negative. They are formed when a task or behaviour is repeated over time.

This enables the thinking part of the brain (the pre-frontal cortex) to conserve energy through reducing its need for active attention and processing. Effectively, the brain is saying 'I have done this before – no need to pay conscious attention to this then!'.

The more repetitions an action has, the stronger the habit, until very little, if any conscious thought is given to the task. This is termed being *unconsciously competent*, and an example would be driving a car after much experience.

An example of a habit that can have negative consequences is not wearing eye protection when using a disc cutter because the past is used to justify present actions. The worker has not been injured before so argues that they will not be injured now. Similar arguments are often put forward for many self-protective and safety-focused equipment and practices.

Similarly, a positive habit can be formed by communicating the benefits and consciously ensuring that eye protection is worn. This could be achieved through raising awareness via posters or stickers on the disc cutter, keeping eye protection with the disc cutter, or spoken reminders from work colleagues and managers. When encouraged and reinforced through these or similar measures, wearing eye protection becomes a comfortable habit and the expected norm.

8.5.1.3 Values, beliefs, expectations, attitudes and behaviour

We all have our own values and beliefs (attitudes) that underlie how we think and then drive the way we act and behave.

Being able to influence these areas is a significant management responsibility, which can be achieved through day-to-day working practice, the level and manner of communication and the delivery of any structured programme to address health and safety interventions.

Whilst the commitment of managers can send a powerful positive message regarding behavioural culture, a lack of commitment can be equally but negatively powerful.

Case study material suggests that low expectations and poor leadership from management can create negative attitudes and a lack of trust from employees. This in turn can result in poor methods of working resulting in poor health and safety performance.

8.5.2 The challenge

Some **potential barriers to progress** that have been identified from existing behavioural safety programmes are shown below.

- Management promoting a negative or passive message, making the workforce believe that it is collecting unnecessary data or that the information will never provide solutions.
- Overreliance on off the shelf solutions and therefore not fully owning the ongoing development of the programme.
- Middle managers either excluded from communication or not understanding the programme.
- Processes not reaching their potential because they are time-consuming and seen as stopping people from getting on with the job without consideration of the huge potential benefits.
- Processes that generate committees, create databases and induce an overload that the majority of small and medium businesses find difficult to resource.
- Organisations fully understanding that behavioural safety approaches are not short-term solutions but may be 'a change in the way we do things round here' that will need an effective investment of resource and commitment.
- A lack of trust leading workers to feel that they will be blamed in some way.
- An existing environment of poor industrial relationships or grievance procedures.

Some **enablers to progress** are shown below.

- Commitment of executives, directors and management to the programme implementation.
- Middle managers' involvement in, and understanding of, the behavioural safety programme objectives.
- Sufficient resources at all levels with which to support work, materials and training.
- A good level of trust between managers and frontline workers.
- The absence of industrial relations issues.
- Existing involvement of the workforce in health and safety practice.
- Innovative and new practice features to the programme on a regular (for example, annual) basis.

Recognising the importance of management commitment to a behavioural safety programme is vital to determine the successful implementation of that programme.

Induction for all: enabling progress on a behavioural safety programme

A
08

8.6 Key stages in a behavioural safety programme

Following research, The Keil Centre produced a report for the HSE, *Strategies to promote safe behaviour as part of a health and safety management system*. This offers the following model of how programmes may be implemented within organisations. Not all elements need to be included in all programmes; this is for guidance and adaptation as appropriate.

For further information refer to the HSE website.

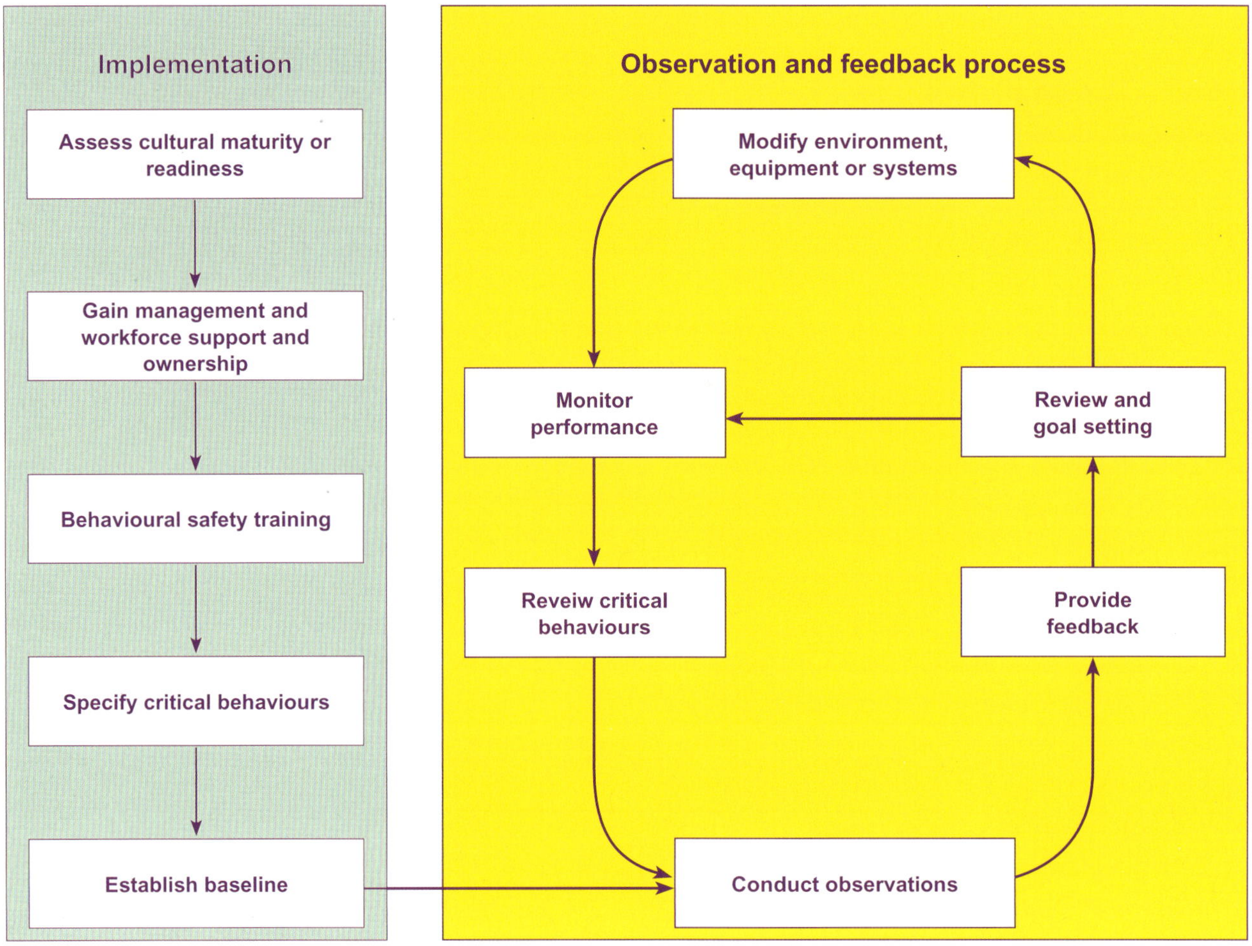

Overview of a behavioural safety programme

8.6.1 Implementation

8.6.1.1 Assess cultural maturity or readiness

At this first stage, the organisation would assess whether it is ready to commit to the implementation of a behavioural safety programme.

This is the stage where potential challenges to success are identified and addressed. This could include an organisational restructure or relocation. It could also highlight and benchmark management commitment and communication processes, by holding workshops, issuing questionnaires or simply through one-to-one interviews.

8.6.1.2 Management and workforce support and ownership

Management and workforce support is crucial for the success of the programme. It defines the culture within which the behavioural safety work occurs and can be encouraged through early involvement of all individuals.

Involvement is generally an emotional response and depends both on the commitment of the individual and the organisation's support and appreciation of their input, views and opinions. People will need to see that they carry influence and can impact on the style and content of the programme to be implemented.

Success of the programme will also depend on the opportunities for individuals involved in managing the programme, or in acting as behavioural safety champions. Not everyone can fulfil these roles and so the organisation may create a process for recruiting to a steering group or to co-ordinator roles. Volunteers can be requested and consideration given to representatives from the entire workforce.

Many programmes require that observations are made of colleagues carrying out tasks. These observations are generally carried out by frontline workers and identify issues relevant to behavioural safety practice and the overall programme. Training is required for these observers to record information, deliver feedback and focus on the objectives that are critical for continuous improvement.

8.6.1.3 Behavioural safety training

Training managers and workers in the understanding of behavioural safety tools and objectives is crucial to programme success.

At the most basic level, this can be awareness training, whilst co-ordinators, managers and those carrying out the main responsibilities will require more in-depth information.

Some programmes train all staff, whereas others train a minority of employees. Decisions regarding this are taken on the basis of internal knowledge and resource (people, financial and material) and the depth of the programme itself.

8.6.1.4 Specifying critical safety behaviours

Behavioural safety programmes focus on developing a checklist of critical safety behaviours that is completed by the trained observers.

Critical health and safety behaviours are identified through a number of different means. These include, but are not solely based on, the analysis of previous accident and incident reports.

Additional information can also be gained from other sources. These can include reviewing previous risk assessments (such as COSHH) and audits, in addition to formal and informal input from frontline staff and managers. Near-miss or dangerous occurrence reports are equally valid sources of critical safety behaviours.

Preparation that focuses solely on formal reporting is important but limited in scope. This will exclude critically unsafe behaviours that have not yet resulted in serious consequences but which hide latent risk.

It is vital that critical safety behaviours and their measures are sufficiently well defined to enable meaningful observations to be made and recorded.

Formal and informal reporting are significant areas of research when defining the critical safety behaviours to be addressed by the programme. Important contributions to this process can be made from a number of levels within an organisation.

8.6.1.5 Establishing a benchmark

The final preparatory element involves identifying a baseline, or benchmarking where the organisation is currently, in relation to the selected critical safety behaviours.

This is established through conducting observations of these areas in practice. A benchmark will enable review and evaluation of the programme's effectiveness to be more clearly defined.

8.6.2 Continuous process of observation and feedback

After the implementation phase, this next continuous stage of observation, feedback, goal setting and review commences.

8.6.2.1 Observations

The next stage in the process is conducting observations. This is generally peer-to-peer, but can be done by managers. It is usual for the observer to be provided with a checklist (the critical behaviours identified previously). The observer indicates on the list whether the individual is safe, unsafe or if the behaviour was not observed.

Defining critical safety behaviours clearly at the pre-observation stage and through the benchmarking process will increase quality and meaning clearly during the programme.

8.6.2.2 Feedback

The provision of feedback is an imperative process within the behavioural safety programme, which can survive or flounder dependent on the skills of observers, their style and credibility. For this reason feedback must be considered to be a critical skill and individuals should be trained accordingly.

Feedback most effectively reinforces safe behaviour when it is positive and delivered by someone perceived as credible and knowledgeable by the individual receiving the feedback. Feedback can have a greater or lesser impact depending on the following factors.

- When it is delivered (generally, the closer and more relevant to the observation the more meaningful the feedback).
- The focus of the feedback (this should be on the observed behaviour, not on the individual practising the behaviour).
- Relevance (the feedback should fit the expectations of the person receiving the feedback and with the behaviour under observation).

There are two main types of feedback.

- **Summative feedback** offers more general comment on an individual's overall performance.
- **Formative feedback** provides more detailed information on how they might improve their performance in the future.

The quality of feedback and its style of delivery is critical to the success of a behavioural safety programme. Observers will need to be trained in positive feedback skills in order to contribute as effectively as possible to the behaviour improvement cycle.

8.6.2.3 Goal setting and review

Goal setting is a participative process involving the observer and either the individual or group concerned.

This process can have an important influence in terms of encouraging supporting behavioural change. People are hard-wired to achieve goals, as this feeds into their brain's internal reward system. The aim is to set goals that have the following (SMART) qualities.

- Stated positively (specific).
- Measurable.
- Achievable.
- Realistic.
- Time-bound.

And finally, goals should be within the direct control of the individual. If they do not meet these important criteria, the individual may not be able to achieve the goal set. This can be demoralising, which in turn can have a direct impact on the success of the programme.

Target or goal setting can take place as regularly as is warranted by the critical behaviours themselves; in some instances this might be every week or month. In many instances, it can be undertaken on a pre-scheduled quarterly basis.

Monitor performance. Behavioural safety programmes are monitored over time with focus being the impact of the programme on the initially identified critical safety behaviours. A good measure of success is an improved percentage of observations where behaviour is observed as safe.

If there is little or no change in this measure over time for some or all observations, it will be important to review the specific behaviours with regard to barriers to change. These could be people or product/design related that work against safe behavioural practice.

A **review of critical behaviours** can be carried out within a defined timescale in order to ensure that the programme is still addressing areas that are relevant and improving. Once these have become habitual they may be replaced by other significant critical behaviours, which are developed through the same looped cycle as detailed by this general model.

Once implemented, the success of the programme is highly dependent upon the commitment made, particularly by managers, at each stage of the process. People will value action and communication regarding progress and assume a lack of commitment if these are not carried through as expected.

8.7 Reducing human error and influencing behaviour

People can cause or contribute to accidents, or mitigate the consequences, by failing to carry out a job correctly and hearing but not listening to or understanding health and safety information that is associated with the task, thereby failing to work to expectations.

People do not generally set out to make errors deliberately but they are often set up to fail by the way the brain processes information. For example, errors may occur as a result of the following.

- Stress or fatigue.
- Working long hours without sufficient rest or with erratic shift patterns.
- Slipping into autopilot mode.
- A lack of training.
- Poor design of equipment.
- Unclear or lack of effective procedures.
- Shortcomings in the culture of the organisation.
- Poor decision making, even when aware of the risks.
- Misinterpretation of a situation or inappropriate action taken.
- Poor situational assessment leading to incident escalation.

When confident and knowledgeable to do so, other people (such as workmates, supervisors and managers) can intervene to prevent potential accidents or mitigate their possible effects.

The severity of an accident can be reduced by the effectiveness of the immediate or emergency response. This effectiveness can be improved by planning and appropriate training.

The following are some of the topics that can influence human error and behaviour.

Latent error

An active error for unsafe working at height – failure to intervene carries health and safety risks

8.7.1 Active and latent failures

The consequences of human failure can be immediate or delayed. It is important to have an understanding of active and latent failures and how they impact on health and safety.

- **Active failures** have an immediate consequence and are usually made by frontline people (such as drivers, operators or even the public). In a situation where there is no room for error, these active failures have an immediate impact on health and safety.
- **Latent failures** are caused by actions generally involving people (such as designers, decision makers and managers) whose tasks are removed in time and space from operational works. Latent failures are typically failures in the design, implementation or monitoring of health and safety management systems.

Latent failures can provide a significant potential danger to health and safety. These can be highlighted only through positive safety discussions that utilise the experience and knowledge of the workforce.

The image of the latent error *(above left)* shows graphite blocks fitted in the Hinkley Point B reactors. These blocks have small cracks within them, which has resulted in the reactors being run at 70% power output. It is believed that these cracks could be due to handling the blocks during construction. This has not affected safety, but it has affected productivity. This is a perfect example of a latent error.

Latent failures (such as the examples below) are generally hidden within an organisation until they are triggered by an event likely to have serious consequences.

- Poor design of workplaces, plant and equipment.
- Gaps in supervision.
- Undetected manufacturing defects.
- Maintenance failures.
- Unworkable procedures.
- Clumsy automation.
- Ineffective competency assurance.
- Ineffective training.
- Ineffective communications.
- Uncertainties of role and responsibility.
- Ageing assets, plant, tools and equipment.
- Poor planning (insufficient people/time).
- Poor information on health and safety incidents.

8.7.2 Impact of change

Change of any type within an organisation can create people issues and behavioural issues. For example:

- an organisation may appoint new leaders and managers
- roles can change
- the need to develop new skills and capabilities may increase.

Workers may be uncertain and resistant because of the following.

- Communication and explanation of the change has been limited.
- People do not see the need for change.
- They feel that they will be disadvantaged by the change.

Dealing with these issues on a reactive, case-by-case basis puts the progress of the job, workforce morale, and overall performance of the behavioural approach at risk.

Change is unsettling for people at all levels of an organisation. The manager, or management team, will need to focus on working together and understanding that change can lead to alterations in typical working practice, stressful responses and a potential need for increased communication and support.

Change affects people personally; this can also be a factor in the implementation of a behavioural safety approach.

Individuals (or teams of individuals) will require timely information regarding the following.

- The changes they will see as a result of a behavioural safety programme.
- What will be expected of them during and after the change programme.
- How they and their behaviours will be measured.
- What success or failure will mean for them and those around them.

8.7.3 Leading by example

The implementation of behavioural safety can pose particular problems with a fragmented and mobile workforce, such as that found in the construction industry.

To be successfully implemented on site, the principles of behavioural safety will need to be embedded within the organisation's culture and understood by the workforce and management from the initiation and planning stages.

The foundations, expectations and compliance processes should be communicated, discussed and agreed from the beginning. If employees and contractors are involved, can influence and are provided with the relevant induction, critical safety behavioural standards will be set for the future.

Managers are a critical element within the success or failure of programmes. Non-compliance and the breaking of basic rules (such as not wearing hard hats or safety goggles) sends a message that a behavioural safety approach is not taken seriously, despite policies and procedures to the contrary.

Similarly, when senior managers visit sites, they should receive the same induction and live by the same rules – body language and example can send a powerful message.

8.7.4 Communication style and content

Communication style and content are important elements that contribute significantly to the building of trust. People feel trust when an individual's behaviour and body language is congruent with what is being said – when 'walking the talk' is evident. Our brains are particularly good at picking up on communication signals from others, whether intended or, as can sometimes be the case, unintended.

Communication is at the heart of all that we do, both at work and in our own time. It takes place in many forms and can be transmitted via various media (for example face-to-face, radio, telephone, email or video conferencing). It is essential, especially within our working environment, that we get it right. Barriers to efficient communication may include background noise, the type of language used and sociocultural issues. The potential for confusion and misinterpretation can be high.

In any communication process, it is vital to give the person receiving information the time and space to be able to think and formulate a response. In communication it is the quality, not the quantity, that matters.

8.7.4.1 Verbal and non-verbal communication

During a normal conversation, we usually transmit and receive in three ways.

- What is said (words).
- How it is said (tonality).
- Body language (conscious or not).

During periods of high workload or stress, our body language goes largely unnoticed. This is when the words we use and the way in which we say them become more important. In addition, our listening capability reduces as our workload or stress increases.

- Communication involves both a communicator and a receiver and is generally the responsibility of the communicator.
- What we say, how we say it and when we say it are perceived differently by different individuals.
- Overload of work and stress can be main factors that hinder effective communication. If the receiver is feeling overloaded, communication will need to reflect this. If the message is important then we need to lessen the workload.
- Job-critical communication requires undivided attention by both the communicator and the receiver.
- The most effective communicators will always check that the meaning they intend through their communication is the one that has been received.

There is a difference between hearing and listening. Hearing is a mechanical process involving the way sound waves are translated. Listening is paying attention to what is being said. When we do this, we are able to evaluate the message within the correct context. An appropriate response can then be planned.

Listening is often described as taking place at different levels, from the less attentive Level 1 (conversational listening) to the more engaging Level 4 (deep listening). At this level, the listener is paying as much attention to body language and signals regarding what is not being said as they are to the words that are spoken.

This type of listening takes skill and practice and is the mark of a good communicator. Observers within a behavioural safety programme would find great benefit in becoming listening masters, so they have the potential to pick up on and challenge safety-related information that could otherwise be missed.

8.7.4.2 Questioning skills

How questions are asked can inform the overall effectiveness of a discussion in terms of information shared.

There are several types of question. Those most commonly used are shown in the table below.

Type	Response
Closed	A fact or YES/NO.
Open	Invites an extensive reply.
Leading	Indicates the required answer.
Limiting	Restricts options.
Multiple	Many questions in one – confusion.

It is important to recognise that we are always communicating. Silence can imply annoyance or criticism, for example. Take time to consider and understand the effect of your personal communication style on others.

Some good practices in communication are listed below.

- Control distractions as much as possible.
- Where possible, make visual and eye contact.
- Clearly identify the communicator and receiver.
- Be clear, precise and concise.
- Avoid the use of leading questions.
- Avoid words that could be misinterpreted or that are ambiguous.
- Never assume meaning.
- Always work to confirm that the intended communication has been appropriately understood.
- Encourage inclusive discussion and dialogue.
- Use phonetics for alphanumeric information (for example, 'M for mother').
- Acknowledge communication from the listener (closed loop communication).

8.7.5 Facilitation, coaching and mentoring

Managers and team leaders should be as honest and explicit as possible about what impacts on health and safety within their workplace. This is particularly the case when an organisation is undergoing a change programme.

Facilitation, coaching and mentoring are interventions and support mechanisms through which individuals are encouraged to take responsibility and contribute ideas to the benefit and safety of others and the organisation.

Individual commitment, ownership and accountability for safety is vital to making change happen. Everyone must be willing to accept responsibility for change in the areas they influence or control. It is important that the need to support and be supported through change is also recognised throughout the workforce, as a part of the behavioural safety culture.

Ownership of challenges is often encouraged by involving people in identifying problems and crafting solutions. It is reinforced by coaching and facilitation, incentives and, in some instances, rewards. These can be tangible (for example, financial compensation) or psychological (for example, camaraderie and a sense of shared involvement).

The most effective behavioural change programmes reinforce the core messages of safety through regular, timely engagement and communications that are both inspirational and practicable. Facilitated discussions are targeted to provide employees with the right information at the right time and to solicit their input and feedback.

8.7.6 Staffing levels

Some companies operate with the lowest possible number of people required to achieve their commercial objectives. Margins are tight and contracts are won and lost on cost.

Under these circumstances, people can be stretched beyond acceptable limits. Individuals could have a high workload, working long hours and experiencing high levels of stress and fatigue. Operating without sufficient human resource can result in significant risk to the workforce.

8.7.7 Training and competency

It is likely that a workforce is more effective and efficient if it is:

- ☑ motivated and well trained
- ☑ not under unreasonable time pressure
- ☑ given the correct information and training
- ☑ working with the right, well-maintained equipment.

A good example of working with the correct equipment

Conversely, high workloads and tight timescales often result in training and competency assessments falling by the wayside.

This can lead to ineffective decision making, poor working practices, out-of-date certification of plant, equipment and, of course, a negative effect on people's skills and behavioural safety practice.

As part of managing change, it is essential that a training and competency assessment is carried out so that shortcomings are identified and addressed, and consequently people are not put at risk.

Every company is responsible in law to ensure that people are trained and competent to carry out their tasks. Greater production efficiencies are achieved through correct skill levels and further gains are made in completion times and work output.

8.7.8 Intervention

There are many recorded instances of people failing to intervene when they see an unsafe or illegal act.

Whilst it is fully understandable that someone might not want to become involved in a violent confrontation in the street, in the context of work the personal risk to say, a supervisor who intervenes to prevent someone working unsafely, is generally not as great.

However, the behaviour of supervisors and managers can directly affect the behaviour of operatives. The effect of failing to intervene in an unsafe situation is to condone that activity, practice or behaviour.

This in turn, sends a message to the operatives that the activity concerned is permitted, resulting in potential confusion for site teams and their working practices. Intervention by managers and supervisors is therefore crucial in every case in order to show commitment to, and support for, behavioural safety programmes.

From general research and available information, the reasons for a failure to intervene appear to be split between a **lack of knowledge** that anything is wrong and a **conscious decision** not to take any action.

A
08

8.7.9 Conscious decision

The conscious decision not to intervene may possibly be based upon financial or time considerations. For example, a supervisor might ignore the unsafe use of a ladder because it saves the time and expense of hiring a mobile elevating work platform (MEWP).

However, there may be other personal factors for not intervening.

- ☑ Overload. The supervisor or manager is suffering from a heavy workload and is simply unable to identify the unsafe situation developing.
- ☑ Actions of others, especially other managers or senior managers, can shape the decisions of the supervisor. Usually the fact that no-one else involved in the operation is concerned about it is excuse enough for not getting involved.
- ☑ Ownership of the situation where the supervisor or manager does not actually believe or understand their duties, or where they are not directly in charge of the operation and believe they have no jurisdiction.
- ☑ Where a supervisor or manager lacks knowledge about the task or the important communication skills, then they are less likely to get involved – having the skills to resolve the issue is important.
- ☑ The risk of possibly entering into a situation where they may be required to make a difficult decision that could have a significant effect on the project. The support of senior managers is critical to allow junior managers and supervisors to become involved in safety issues and empower them to take whatever action they deem necessary if an unsafe situation arises. This could even involve the cessation of work until the safety issue is investigated further.

8.7.10 Managing the risk

Making assessments about risks and reaching an informed decision requires the information held within the safety management system.

The process of obtaining information begins with the recognition that the problem exists, and then raises questions to which answers are required.

Deciding on the level of accuracy and precision of the risk and safety assessment will depend on the sampling and measurement methods used in collating the initial risk information. In behavioural terms, this is done through identifying 'what' is happening during an observation and asking 'why'. The 'whats and whys' are analysed and tabulated to identify trends, often by interpreting the data.

Interpretation is based on the personal perception of what has been observed and so identifying trends can be difficult. Although risk can be quantified as abstract principles, health and safety cannot.

Whilst risk assessment is based on knowledge of the job and past experience, the corresponding judgement on safety is subjective and can be political. It may be possible to obtain group agreement on objective and rational measures of risk for various work. However, there will often be controversy over what are considered to be safe conditions.

Attempting to define acceptable levels of risk immediately raises the question of 'to whom' or 'on what terms' is the risk acceptable?

The distinction between risk and safety is relevant to many organisations and there are a number of factors to be considered in defining the acceptability of risk.

- ☑ **Cost.** Safety is always compromised by available budget yet it costs far more to investigate and restore safe working conditions after an accident than it does to resolve the issues in the first place.
- ☑ **Controls.** Who has control? Those at the place of work should have control over the safety requirements of the task. Ownership of health and safety controls is critical for a safe working environment.
- ☑ **Customs.** Many risks are taken because certain work has always been done that way.
- ☑ **Conditions.** Many people are put at risk because conditions have changed, resulting in longer working hours, tight timescales, lack of resources, workload, fatigue, stress or an ageing workforce. This leads to errors, particularly in plant maintenance.
- ☑ **Consequences.** Managers rarely evaluate in advance the consequences of something going wrong. Often the thought process seems to be 'if it hasn't happened yet, it won't happen at all'.
- ☑ **Benefit.** What benefits does the individual get from taking a short cut, such as an early finish when the job is done?

8.7.11 Benefits of health and safety discussions

One method of enhancing any safe system of work is through frequent and open discussions. The heart of any process is communication, with all involved recognising the value of shared ideas and knowledge. This has the potential to impact positively on bottom-line profits, with individuals and teams working more efficiently towards achieving high-quality business objectives.

The company's image will also benefit if, by the actions exhibited, it is shown to be committed to a safe and healthy working environment, where no-one is injured or becomes ill as a result of coming to work.

An example of good practice communication is for site managers to have an informal 10-minute chat with their employees and/or contractors' supervisors at the start of every day. The manager should encourage them to tell each other where they will be working and how their activity could affect other people. This will help supervisors to plan their day, as well as improving co-ordination, consultation, production and, ultimately, safety.

The aim of a behavioural safety discussion is to identify any difficulties in completing tasks safely and to aid the supervisor, manager and individual in identifying problems and achieve a safe system of work. Participants in the discussion should be encouraged to use open questions, smooth the way forward, be clear in what they are saying, avoid any misunderstanding and proactively resolve issues through positive actions rather than reactively observing unsafe actions.

Those with more knowledge and experience can assist newer colleagues in understanding the hazards around them and stop people putting themselves at risk. Learning through a coaching and mentoring approach can be more effective and less onorous than more formal observation work.

All workers and managers can make valid contributions to discussions on behavioural safety. Do not impose your own thoughts and avoid passing judgement. Above all else, problems or issues should be resolved immediately with someone who has the authority to make the necessary changes.

09

Leadership and worker engagement

Contents

Supporting information

GT 700 Toolbox talks

Overview

This chapter gives a general overview of the principles of leadership and worker engagement. It looks at how these impact on organisations within the construction industry. Additional resource information, tools and techniques are presented, which can inform workplaces and influence leadership and engagement behaviours.

9.1 Introduction

The construction industry is one of the UK's most significant economic sectors, with over 197,500 organisations, of which 90% employ fewer than 10 workers, which are small to medium size enterprises (SMEs). It is also consistently one of the most dangerous sectors to work in, according to Health and Safety Executive (HSE) statistics.

The industry is therefore continually seeking to find innovative ways in which it can reduce ill health and accidents by engaging with its workforce. This has a number of identifiable business benefits, including the promotion of sustainable behaviour change to ensure that health and safety is taken seriously on site.

Success is dependent upon the quality of leadership and management practice within organisations. Commitment and responsibility at all levels is a critical step in the development of a successful, innovative business and proactive worker engagement.

Definitions of leadership vary across organisations and leadership experts. These are largely centred around building relationships and interpersonal skills, focusing on individuals who are:

- ☑ visionary
- ☑ motivational
- ☑ inspirational
- ☑ emotionally intelligent
- ☑ trustworthy
- ☑ natural leaders and communicators
- ☑ driven
- ☑ ambitious
- ☑ resilient – able to deal with pressure and failure.

There is a need for a range of skills and knowledge. These fall into three main areas.

- ☑ Appropriate technical and professional skills, relevant to the organisation.
- ☑ Commercial and financial, including a high level of business acumen and experience (both success and failure).
- ☑ Skills in people management and development (coaching and feedback, communication and team management).

Good leadership is seen as encompassing a strong mix of all these skills, with weaknesses in one area being seen to diminish the overall capability of the leader.

Research has identified various traits, differentiating good from outstanding leadership. These outstanding leaders are described as having the following abilities.

- ☑ Being able to think and act systematically.
- ☑ Understanding the whole and the connection between internal work and the external environment.
- ☑ Seeing people as the route to performance.
- ☑ Building relationships and provide an environment in which they can shine.
- ☑ Being self-confident without being arrogant.
- ☑ Being professional.
- ☑ Having personal humility.
- ☑ Providing appropriate space and the support to allow people to think and make decisions.

A vital task facing the leader of tomorrow is that of engaging workers within the day-to-day operation of their own roles in order to support achievement of the wider organisational objectives.

Leaders who are able to bring the full range of worker motivation, creativity, skills and knowledge to their businesses are those whose organisations succeed in an increasingly competitive and fastmoving market place.

Leadership development, worker engagement and business performance are strongly linked. In organisations where management and leadership development are embedded, employee engagement levels are higher.

9.2 Important points

Industry and the HSE have produced a *Leadership and worker involvement toolkit*. It is based on **10 key principles**.

1.	**Don't walk by**	It is everyone's responsibility on site to prevent any unsafe acts and conditions that they witness from turning into accidents as soon as they see them. Talk to the person(s) involved and draw their attention to the risks.
2.	**STOP**	All workers should be encouraged to stop working whenever they feel unsafe, even if their reasons for doing so turn out to be unfounded. Better to STOP than to have an accident.
3.	**A safe working environment drives safe behaviour**	If you expect your workers to work in a safe way, you need to make sure that you do all you can to make the environment they work in as safe as possible.
4.	**Don't blame the worker until you have accounted for all causes**	The causes of unsafe ways of working, accidents, incidents and ill health do not always stop with the worker. The problem can often be traced back to less obvious causes (such as decisions made by management and the wider organisation). Avoid blaming the worker without having considered the full range of possible causes.
5.	**Use your workforce for ideas**	Your workers can have a more accurate idea of which efforts to improve health and safety may work than you, your management or other experts. They have to deal with the issues every day. Use and include them.
6.	**Change does not usually happen overnight**	Do not expect quick wins. Improvements are likely to emerge over time, but only if you stick with it.
7.	**Knowledge is not enough**	Simply telling workers that something is wrong, or is a risk, is not enough. They also need to know why, and how to avoid harm if they are to act on the information that you provide.
8.	**Lead by example**	Your behaviour sends strong signals to your workers as to how they should behave. If you carry out your job in a safe way, your workers are more likely to work in safe ways. If you do not then your workers will not.
9.	**Encourage co-operation**	Treat your sub-contractors in the same way as direct employees. Encourage different sub-contractors and trades to proactively communicate with each other. Getting consistency in standards will then be that much easier.
10.	**Don't neglect occupational health**	If you look after the health as well as the safety of your workers now, you are less likely to store up problems for either you or your workforce in the future.

9.3 Understanding worker engagement

A
09

9.3.1 Work Foundation

The Work Foundation, a provider of research-based analysis, knowledge exchange and policy advice in the UK, defines employee (worker) engagement in this way:

> **Employee engagement describes employees' emotional and intellectual commitment to their organisation and its success. Engaged employees experience a compelling purpose and meaning in their work and give of their discrete effort to advance the organisation's objectives.**

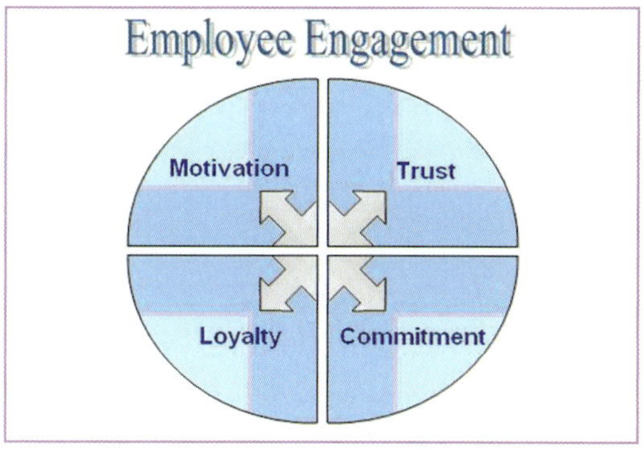

A typical representation of factors influenced by employee (worker) engagement strategies

Effectively, engagement is about how workers behave at work and the impact this has on their own performance and that of the organisation. This is particularly in respect of the discretionary effort that they apply within the workplace.

Within the construction industry, there is a specific focus on health and safety within worker engagement practice.

The HSE's health and safety strategy of the UK talks of 'genuine management workforce partnership based on trust, respect and co-operation' and 'the combined involvement of management and health and safety representatives in inspections, investigations and risk assessments'.

www.

For further information refer to the Work Foundation website.

The HSE also identifies the growing body of evidence which:

> **indicates that effective worker involvement and consultation on health and safety has a positive impact on both individual workers and organisations as a whole. Workers who are involved are also more committed and feel more valued. This is reflected in greater job satisfaction and a lower likelihood of leaving the organisation. For the construction company the result is improved health and safety, which translates into reduced sickness absence, increased productivity and quality, and reduced staff turnover.**

www. **For further information refer to the worker engagement section of the HSE website.**

9.3.2 Construction Industry Advisory Committee

The Construction Industry Advisory Committee (CONIAC) offers a specific declaration with regard to worker engagement and health and safety, shown below.

Statement of principle

- ☑ Every construction worker has a right to work in places where risks to their health and safety are properly controlled.
- ☑ Every worker should have a voice and will be given opportunities to influence health and safety in the places they work.
- ☑ We commit to actively promoting positive relationships between workers and their representatives, employers, designers clients and those having control of construction work. We recognise the role that unions and safety representatives play in improving worker health and safety consultation.

We will:

- ☑ expect **all** workers to get involved
- ☑ encourage clients, employers, designers, project managers and others in control of construction work to ensure workers are listened to and given real opportunities to help improve their working conditions
- ☑ ensure that sufficient resources, including training, are made available to all sectors of the construction industry to improve worker consultation
- ☑ develop and share good practice in the industry.

Our aim is to achieve a long-term culture change in the construction industry, in order to improve working conditions for everyone.

www. **For further information refer to the CONIAC section of the HSE website.**

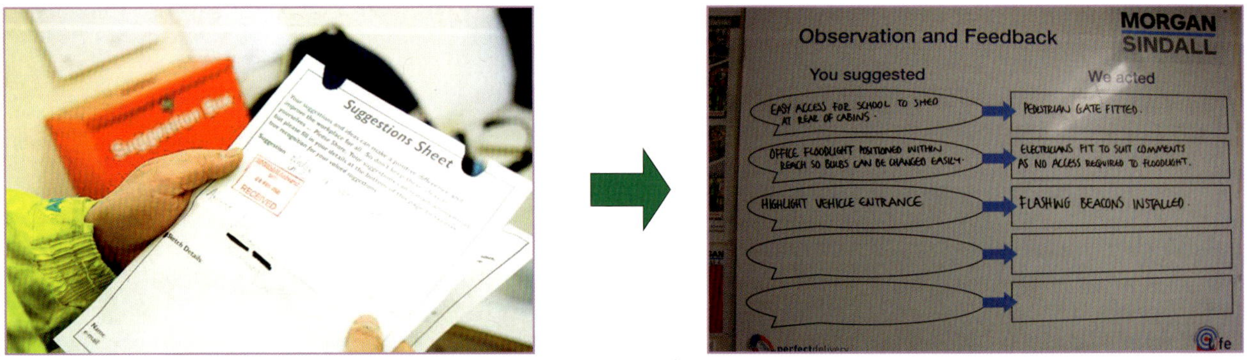

A 'you suggested – we acted' board helps workers see that concerns are being listened to and acted upon

The HSE's strategy for managing health and safety in the UK includes 'genuine management workforce partnership based on trust, respect and co-operation'.

9.3.3 Barriers to workforce engagement

Research by the HSE has identified that barriers to workforce engagement are in many ways similar to behavioural change barriers.

- ☑ The disparate, transient and multicultural nature of the workforce on site.
- ☑ Working style associated with a results-focused and target-driven industry.
- ☑ Disincentives to report health and safety issues that may result in future loss of projects and income.
- ☑ Lack of client motivation to adopt worker engagement practices.
- ☑ Appropriateness of off-the-shelf solutions, given the variance in industry-related organisations.
- ☑ Lack of management commitment to, or understanding of, the benefits of worker engagement practice.

The following list shows some potential solutions to **overcoming barriers**.

Leadership is about vision, motivation and moving towards a common goal

- ☑ Treating each engagement project as a separate strategy.
- ☑ Training relevant individuals in behavioural change and worker engagement skills.
- ☑ Focusing on the supply chain as a route for delivery of worker engagement.
- ☑ Including the supply chain and sub-contractors in behavioural change and engagement training.
- ☑ Running launch events for worker engagement and building in behavioural change and worker engagement standards in to sub-contracts.
- ☑ Building a preferred supply chain.

In addition, there is a real focus on worker engagement tools that can be employed to aid implementation of good practice. This is particularly the case for the construction industry, where a lack of worker engagement is directly linked to the potential for health and safety incidents.

9.4 Tools and techniques, hints and tips

9.4.1 Leadership and worker involvement toolkit

As a part of its significant focus in this area, the HSE website hosts the *Leadership and worker involvement toolkit.*

This toolkit is designed for the SME businesses that employ between 11 and 250 workers and contractors. It has been developed by the construction industry's Leadership and Worker Engagement forum to support contractors and managers in improving their health and safety performance through engaging with their workforce.

www.

For access to the *Leadership and worker involvement toolkit* refer to the HSE website.

The toolkit itself comprises seven steps, each of which is designed to be worked through in order. Each step offers practical tools that can be taken away and used as the individual requires. Guidance from the HSE advises against completing the toolkit in one go; instead, it is recommended that individuals take time to explore each step and to consider how these might support their own worker involvement activities.

Screenshot of the leadership and worker involvement toolkit

The seven steps	
Step 1	Assess how you're doing.
Step 2	Find the root of the issues.
Step 3	Make it fit with what you do.
Step 4	Lead this in your company.
Step 5	What's in it for your team?
Step 6	How your team can carry it out.
Step 7	Make it last.

The HSE also offers guidance and materials for workers who as individuals wish to learn more about how they can become proactively engaged within the workplace. Called *Safe and sound at work: do your bit* this takes the form of links to advisory information with ideas for actions that anyone can take.

The toolkit is based on 10 key principles, each of which supports good practice leadership and worker involvement in relation to health and safety (*refer to 9.2.*).

9.4.2 The Best Companies – Engagement survey

'The Best Companies' is a specialist in workplace engagement. Each January it produces a listing, published through a major Sunday newspaper, of the 100 best companies to work for.

It uses a survey methodology to identify workplace performance and good practice according to eight vital factors. These are the factors which, through the survey results themselves, have been found to be critical factors in workplace engagement.

- **Leadership.** How employees feel about the head of the organisation, senior managers, and the organisation's values and principles.
- **My manager.** How employees feel about, and communicate with, their direct manager.
- **Personal growth.** What employees feel about training and their future prospects.
- **Wellbeing.** How employees feel about stress, pressure at work, and work life balance.
- **My team.** Employees' feelings towards their immediate colleagues and how well they work together.
- **Giving something back.** The extent to which employees feel their organisation has a positive impact on society.
- **My company.** The level of engagement employees have for their job and organisation.
- **Fair deal.** How happy employees are with their pay and benefits.

Engaging workers

- Be patient. The process of engaging workers takes time; those that have done it say that while there were some results within a year, it was nearer five years before they were happy that the process was embedded. Nor is the process **ever** complete.
- Make sure the directors and senior managers visibly support a worker involvement culture. They can do this by addressing meetings, sending out messages, instructing managers, and 'talking the talk and walking the walk'.
- Explain why you want to talk to workers and what it involves.
- Run an employee opinion survey and be seen to act rapidly on a couple of suggestions or shortcomings. That way, employees will start to appreciate that the employer is serious about worker engagement.
- When receiving suggestions, always ensure that the person making the suggestion receives feedback, even if the answer is 'sorry, we can't, and these are the reasons why'. The fact that the employee's views are treated seriously is usually more important than agreeing with them. Linked to this, ensure that you publicise responses to employees' suggestions.
- You need to talk to personnel at all levels of an organisation, using different tactics for different groups and even individuals. For example, email might elicit suggestions from office-based workers, but may be less appropriate in a warehouse. There were, however, fascinating examples (such as steel-encased PC kiosks on the factory floor) that combined processes, holiday forms, emails and worker engagement in health and safety.
- Be visible. Walk around. Talk to staff. Take small numbers of staff on regular safety walk rounds.
- An anonymised system of reporting complaints or problems is helpful in the initial stages of embracing worker engagement, but appears to be rarely used once the culture is embedded.
- Ensure you take the views of shift-workers and part-time staff into account.
- Take staff to another organisation where worker engagement is working.
- Worker engagement in health and safety will not happen without a genuine no-blame culture.
- Ensure representatives have training in how to be a representative (covering eliciting views, presenting a case, feeding back to colleagues) as well as in health and safety. Even in most of the best examples, representatives are often not trained in this role.
- People are generally reluctant to volunteer as a representative of employee safety, and it may be worth having a quiet word with employees you think would do a good job. Assertive and confident individuals will facilitate better engagement than 'yes' people. Informal leaders (who workers already turn to for advice) may either make good representatives themselves or be important in lending credibility to the notion and practice of engagement. Consider also offering inducements and rewards (financial or otherwise).
- Make sure that any joint health and safety committees have a workable balance of employee representatives and managers. Managers should consider absenting themselves from part of a meeting in order to ensure that representatives are not intimidated from speaking out. This should not undermine the case for strong leadership from the top, and the need for such temporary absence will diminish as representatives grow in experience and confidence.
- Ensure your managers and staff are trained in soft skills as well as hard skills.

Worker involvement in health and safety will not happen unless there is a no-blame culture in place.

9.5 Leadership styles

Research has recognised that leadership styles come from the use of emotional intelligence (EI): being acutely aware of the environment, the emotional needs of individuals involved and adjusting leadership style to suit the setting.

These styles can be seen below. They summarise the techniques, scenarios of when they work best and the impact on the organisation and its goals.

9.5.1 Coercive leader

The coercive leader, which is the most aggressive of the leadership styles, expects and demands immediate compliance to their orders. This is a style that is designed to accomplish tasks by ordering and dictating, even demeaning their followers at times.

This style is often used in situations where the company requires an urgent and complete turnaround attempt; it is important to note that group discussions are not encouraged or generally permissible under this style. An example could be during disasters, or when enforcing health and safety compliance improvements under law.

This style should only be used for short and immediate timeframes, as the medium and longer term impact can be negative.

9.5.2 Authoritative leader

The authoritative leader establishes themselves as being the expert in the company; the person who creates the vision and leads the way.

Authoritative leaders lead the team to the vision and encourage team members to achieve their goals. This style can be particularly effective in times when a new direction is needed: for someone to come up with the vision and the way forward.

9.5.3 Affiliative leader

The affiliate leader establishes a style of building teams and of putting employees first. This individual offers a significant amount of praise and feedback and there is normally a good sense of team spirit encouraged by this style.

This can be most effective when there are situations of low morale and poor teamwork. Utilising this method will, in the longer term, create good team bonding and heightened team performance.

One negative aspect of this is the potential for poor performance to be accepted, as the leader may avoid difficult conversations in order to avoid conflict.

9.5.4 Democratic leader

The democratic leader will focus on the team as the decision makers to create improvements. Communication is a core skill within this model, whereby all opinions are listened to as a group. The role of the democratic leader is to act as chairperson to encourage effective team decision making.

This style produces a work environment that employees can feel good about, with heightened morale levels. Workers feel that their opinion matters, and because of that feeling they are more committed to achieving the goals and objectives of the organisation.

It will be important to remember that decision making will need to be a focus of attention for this style.

9.5.5 Pacesetting leader

The pacesetting leadership method comes into its own and can be extremely effective when team members are motivated and competent within their roles. These leaders set very high performance standards for themselves and the group and lead by example.

Like the coercive model, this is another of the leadership styles that cannot be sustained for a long time as workers can often burn out due to the energy needed to sustain this approach.

A good example of when to use this style is when a group has been functioning as an effective team for a period of time and is now performing in a strong team culture. At this stage the leader may wish to step things up and move to a new level of performance for a specific project.

9.5.6 Coaching leader

In the coaching leadership style the leader focuses on supporting others in their personal development, and in their job-related activities, towards a goal. The leader helps team members to up-skill and become successful in their development, coaching and mentoring to ensure successful knowledge transfer and independent role development.

This style can be described as a generic management style and works well when the employee is willing to work on both their strengths and areas for development. Whilst this can come across as micromanaging the team, when done well from a trained leader this is an effective style to develop a culture of inclusivity, engagement and learning.

9.5.7 Transformational leadership

This describes a style of leadership that enhances the motivation, morale and performance of followers through a variety of mechanisms. These include connecting the follower's sense of identity and self to the mission and the collective identity of the organisation; being an inspiring role model; challenging followers to take greater ownership for their work, and understanding individual strengths and weaknesses of followers, so the leader can align team members with tasks that optimise their performance.

9.5.8 Transactional leadership

Transactional leadership styles are more concerned with maintaining the normal flow of operations. Transactional leadership can be described as 'keeping the balls in the air'.

Transactional leaders use both disciplinary power and a number of different incentives to motivate employees to perform at their best. The term *transactional* refers to the fact that this type of leader essentially motivates subordinates by exchanging performance for rewards.

A transactional leader generally tends not to look ahead in strategically guiding an organisation to a position of market leadership; instead, these managers are solely concerned with making sure everything flows smoothly today.

9.5.9 In summary

While coercion and pacesetting do perhaps have their uses, research suggests that these styles can damage the organisation's working atmosphere over time. This will ultimately reduce flexibility and employee commitment. So the aim is to use these only when absolutely required (in a case of a health and safety emergency for example) and within a small timeframe.

The most effective leader is one who can use different styles in different situations.

The message is clear: from research, employee surveys and case study information, there is no doubt that the quality and effectiveness of management and leadership has a significant impact on the level to which workers are engaged within their jobs. This in turn has direct consequences for health and safety measures within organisations.

9.6 National Occupational Standards – Management and leadership

The National Occupational Standards (NOS) for management and leadership are statements of good practice that outline the performance criteria, related skills, knowledge and understanding required to effectively carry out various management and leadership functions.

They are produced by the Management Standards Centre (MSC), the Government-recognised standards-setting body for the management and leadership areas.

The MSC describes the standards as:

> **The activities/functions of management and leadership at various levels of responsibility and complexity. Therefore, they are relevant to anyone for whom management and leadership is, to a greater or lesser extent, part of their work. This applies to managers and leaders in all sizes and types of organisation, and in all industries and sectors.**

Accessing this information will provide the opportunity to see the suite of standards most relevant to different levels of management and leadership. These standards are generic and so equally applicable to management and leadership practice within organisations of all sizes and across all sectors.

www.

For further information refer to the standards section of the Management Standards Centre website.

9.7 Legislative requirements

The Health and Safety at Work Act 2(4) allows for regulations to be made for the appointment of safety representatives from recognised trade unions.

As a result the **Safety Representatives and Safety Committees Regulations** were introduced. These were later amended by the Management of Health and Safety at Work Regulations.

The **Health and Safety (Consultation with Employees) Regulations** widened the scope of the duties of employers to consult with employees who are not members of a trade union.

Additionally, the Construction (Design and Management) Regulations have placed an increased emphasis on consultation. There is also a specific duty on the principal contractor to consult and engage with workers.

Where an employee is a member of a recognised trade union, the Safety Representatives and Safety Committees Regulations will apply, together with the Health and Safety at Work Act. Where there is no recognised trade union membership representation, the Health and Safety (Consultation with Employees) Regulations apply.

9.7.1 Legal requirements for communicating with all employees

Employers must inform employees of the following points.

- The main terms and conditions of employment.
- Changes in terms and conditions of employment.
- The reason for dismissing them from their job, where applicable.
- Certain business matters (for example, when there is a significant change in the way the business operates).
- Health and safety issues and consultation with the workforce on health and safety.

These Health and Safety (Consultation with Employees) Regulations and the Safety Representatives and Safety Committees Regulations will apply to most workplaces.

www.

The Health and Safety Executive (HSE) has developed easy-to-use guidance that shows the relationship between the two sets of regulations and how they may affect businesses and their workforces.

The business may benefit from consulting employees on a regular basis and making staff aware of ways they can contribute ideas and raise concerns. The business does not need to have complex structures for consultation – often ad hoc groups can work best.

For effective consultation consider the following.

- Explaining final decisions, particularly when employees' views are rejected.
- Giving credit and recognition to those who provide information that improves a decision.
- Ensuring that the issues for consultation are relevant to the group of employees discussing them.
- Avoiding minor issues and petty grievances.
- Making the outcome of the meeting available to everyone.

Good communication processes will make employee engagement easier and more effective. The main aspects of achieving that include the following.

- Involving the workforce in building a set of values by which the company will operate.
- Building dialogue with the workforce by communicating regularly and openly about matters that affect the business. This will build credibility and create an environment of trust.
- Involving the workforce in the most important employee issues as soon as possible.
- Avoiding leaks of information or rumours spreading.
- Living the values.

In the construction industry it is especially important to ensure that this communication is effective and timely, particularly in relation to health and safety.

All workers, including those in the construction industry, have a right to be consulted on the work they do, to be given adequate information and training to carry out this work in a safe and healthy manner and to have decent site facilities. Being directly involved in the process, employees often see problems as they emerge.

Recent years have seen a large increase in the numbers of foreign workers in all sectors. The increasing size of the European Union has caused an influx of labour for whom English may not be their first language and communication can become more difficult, leading to a greater risk of misunderstanding. These workers must be fully engaged and consulted on matters of health and safety at work: employers must find adequate mechanisms to do this. Similar consideration should be given to other workers who have difficulties in communicating.

The Construction (Design and Management) Regulations place a duty on principal contractors to make and maintain arrangements to enable effective co-operation between all parties on site, and to consult with all workers on site. Consultation means not only giving information to workers, but also listening and taking account of what workers say, before making health and safety decisions. Part of the purpose of consultation is to make sure the measures taken on site to protect workers' health and safety are effective.

Principal contractors are encouraged to develop a variety of methods of communication and consultation with the workforce to develop collaboration and trust. When matters of concern are raised by workers these should be taken seriously and feedback given. Evidence that this is happening provides assurance that effective worker engagement is in place.

Involving the workforce in identifying and controlling risks is crucial in preventing accidents. Whether projects are notifiable or not, contractors have a duty to inform workers of their procedures for stopping work in the event of serious and imminent danger, and to provide training where necessary. This should make sure workers are willing and able to intervene to prevent an accident from happening.

A toolkit has been produced by the construction industry's Leadership and Worker Engagement forum to help contractors and managers learn how to make health and safety improvements in their businesses *(refer to 9.4.1)*.

9.7.2 Safety Representatives and Safety Committees Regulations

A summary of the **role of the safety representative** is shown below.

- Representing their members' interests in matters of health, safety and welfare.
- Carrying out the statutory functions outlined in the regulations.
- Representing their members in consultation with the HSE or other enforcing authority.

Functions of the safety representative include the following.

- Consulting with the employer.
- Investigating and reporting significant hazards and dangerous occurrences.
- Investigating accidents in the workplace.
- Representation on general health and safety matters.
- Receiving complaints by employees.
- Representation in consultation with the HSE or other enforcing authority.
- Receiving information from the enforcing authority.
- Attendance at meetings of safety committees.
- Inspecting the workplace.

For further information on consulting workers on health and safety refer to L146.

A
09

9.7.3 The Equality Act

Equality and diversity are issues of rising importance that the construction industry needs to acknowledge and address. This has been brought into sharper focus following the recent changes to legislation, with the introduction of the Equality Act, which became law in October 2010. It replaces previous legislation (such as the Race Relations Act and the Disability Discrimination Act) and ensures consistency in what employers need to do to make the workplace a fair environment and to comply with the law.

The Equality Act covers the same groups that were protected by existing equality legislation – age, disability, gender reassignment, race, religion or belief, sex, sexual orientation, marriage and civil partnership, pregnancy and maternity – but extends some protections to groups not previously covered, and also strengthens particular aspects of equality law.

The Equality Act is a mixture of rights and responsibilities that have:

- **stayed the same** – for example, direct discrimination still occurs when someone is treated less favourably than another person because of a protected characteristic
- **changed** – for example, employees can now complain of harassment even if it is not directed at them, if they can demonstrate that it creates an offensive environment for them
- **been extended** – for example, associative discrimination (direct discrimination against someone because they associate with another person who possesses a protected characteristic) covers age, disability, gender reassignment and sex, as well as race, religion and belief and sexual orientation
- **been introduced for the first time** – for example, the concept of discrimination arising from disability, which occurs if a person with a disability is treated unfavourably because of something arising as a consequence of their disability.

Whilst construction sites can be hazardous places of work for anyone, employers must accept their legal duties and make reasonable adjustments within the working environment to ensure that fairness is achieved and discrimination does not occur.

e.g. Impacts of equality and diversity on the health and safety environment

Equality and diversity impact on the health and safety environment because:

- ☑ staff who are bullied or suffer harassment at work may not feel safe or act in a rational manner – bullying/harassment, including initiation ceremonies and fooling around, can also involve unsafe acts
- ☑ a person may have a visual, hearing or speech impairment that could, for example, make communication of risks difficult
- ☑ a person may have restricted mobility and therefore have difficulty in walking, climbing ladders, lifting or carrying out certain aspects of work
- ☑ poorly fitting personal protective equipment (PPE) for employees can be uncomfortable, impede mobility and/or movement necessary for safe working (for example, a person's physique may mean standard issue PPE is too small or large).

A part of making reasonable adjustments is likely to be consultation between the employer and the person(s) on how certain situations will be managed.

Employers have a responsibility to ensure their employees are supported and not discriminated against. Supervisors and managers must be aware of these responsibilities and the way to eliminate or effectively manage situations if they arise.

In addition employers have a responsibility to ensure every employee understands safety information and messages, both in terms of language used and the workplace culture. Ensuring clear messaging can result in better working conditions and practices and a more productive team approach.

10

Inspections and audits

Contents

Supporting information

G: Checklists and forms

GT 700 Toolbox talks

Overview

Measurement is a vital step in the management process and forms the basis of continual improvements. If measures (such as site inspections or health and safety audits) are not carried out correctly, there is no reliable information to show if health and safety risks are being managed.

This chapter outlines the types of measurement and the benefits of monitoring health and safety.

10.1 Introduction

Employers and employees have a moral, social and legal duty to prevent accidents by every practicable means available to them. The costs of getting it wrong to a firm, its employees and others affected may be great and provide ample motivation to all involved to reduce the risks to health and safety.

Motivation must, however, be translated into effective action, and this can only be achieved by the commitment of management and supervisors at all levels. It is well established and documented that accidents can be prevented by:

- ☑ **identifying** the hazards that employees face within the workplace
- ☑ **understanding** how accidents are caused by unsafe acts, unsafe systems of work and unsafe conditions on site
- ☑ taking steps to **control** the activity of the worker, the work method and the workplace.

Employers, managers, supervisors and safety representatives all have equally important roles to play. By obtaining and providing information through the **inspection, investigation and examination** of the workplace, they can help provide a basis for effective management action to promote safer and healthier workplaces, and induce a greater awareness of health, safety and welfare on the part of all concerned. There are strong links between this topic content and the need to speak with employees on matters of health and safety.

10.2 Important points

- ☑ Health and safety inspections and audits can become a productive part of consultation between management and the workforce.
- ☑ While they are often carried out by a health and safety professional, they do not have to be.
- ☑ The successful outcome of any inspection or audit is that remedial actions are put in place where shortcomings have been identified.
- ☑ Workplace inspections are most effective when carried out against a predetermined checklist incorporating some method of recording the findings.
- ☑ Whereas workplace inspections tend to be a 'snapshot in time', an audit is a thorough examination not only of the site conditions prevailing at any one time but also of the:
  - commitment of management to health and safety
  - procedures that underpin the health and safety management system.
- ☑ The emphasis on contractors being able to demonstrate their competence in matters of health and safety management potentially puts a greater importance on them being able to show that inspections and audits are carried out and acted upon.

A
10

10.3 Measuring performance

There are several ways in which a company may measure the effectiveness of its health and safety performance.

- ☑ Evaluating the effectiveness of earlier risk assessments.
- ☑ Gathering and evaluating information on the number of accidents over a reference period, their causes and effects.
- ☑ The investigation of worker feedback on near misses and dangerous occurrences.
- ☑ Gathering information on reportable diseases.
- ☑ The results of health and safety audits.
- ☑ The results of inspections, whether regular, unannounced or specific.
- ☑ The level of health and safety awareness among employees in the form of feedback from training courses and safety committee meetings.
- ☑ Benchmarking against previous audits.

10.4 Monitoring

Employers are required to monitor performance. There are two types of monitoring used in auditing and inspecting: proactive and reactive.

10.4.1 Proactive monitoring

Proactive monitoring measures the current level of compliance with legislation and company procedures. It can take the following forms.

- ☑ Health and safety inspections.
- ☑ Pre-use checks.
- ☑ Safety tours.
- ☑ Hazard-spotting exercises.
- ☑ Surveys.
- ☑ Audits.

Health and safety inspections tend to be the site manager's snapshot of the health and safety standards on site at any one time. Alternatively, or in addition, a company's health and safety adviser or director may carry out these inspections.

A health and safety inspection or audit may examine the big picture or concentrate on only one feature; irrespective of who carries them out, they must have the knowledge to enable them to detect unsafe situations and the authority to ensure they are rectified.

10.4.2 Reactive monitoring

This type of monitoring investigates anything that has actually happened. Accidents, incidents, near misses and illness resulting in serious injuries and fatalities, including health hazards, are too often a feature of work in the construction industry. The proactive management of health and safety should serve to keep such incidents to a minimum.

It should not be forgotten that a near miss today could be a potential accident tomorrow. Supervisors have an important role to play in both proactive and reactive monitoring.

10.5 Inspections

Formal inspections at reasonably regular intervals should augment the site manager's day-to-day checks, inspections and examinations, which occur as part of any task. These should follow a properly designed checklist for the systematic inspection of the workplace.

A health, safety and environment inspection report and a weekly project inspection form can be found in Section G: *Checklists and forms.*

The advantages of regular inspections are that they ensure good housekeeping is maintained within the workplace and that awareness is developed, amongst employees at all levels, of the need to promote and maintain safety, health and environmental standards. The disadvantage or danger of regular inspections is that they may become a rather mechanical routine for all concerned, and that their impact might be lessened.

Carrying out joint inspections with safety representatives, other members of the team or even nominated workers from different trades or contractors can help to identify issues that may be overlooked during a routine inspection.

Stopping and engaging a two-way conversation with the workforce during inspections is vital so as to understand why they are doing the work the way they are and what issues they have.

This goes a long way in helping to build a positive safety culture, but it is just as important to follow through or feed back on issues. More often than not, they will be able to help find and agree solutions.

Random inspections carried out without any prior notice to the workforce, on different days of the week, at irregular intervals and at different times of the day, avoid the shortcomings of a predictable inspection and help to encourage a continuous interest in safety by all personnel.

In practice, a combination of both regular and random inspections is probably the best course of action.

e.g. **On one project, the site manager carried out his weekly site inspections with a different sub-contract employee. Results of the inspection were jointly presented to the site workforce as a toolbox talk.**

A 10

10.5.1 Safety representatives

In accordance with the **Safety Representatives and Safety Committees Regulations** safety representatives are entitled to inspect the workplace. An Approved Code of Practice (ACoP) and guidance notes have been issued by the HSE to support the relevant regulations. These emphasise areas where safety representatives should reach agreement with their employers.

A safety representative may consider the company's safety inspection procedure to be adequate. In such cases, the representative may only need to seek an agreement with the management that they are involved in any future inspections of the workplace.

However, if the company's arrangements for the inspection of the workplace are thought to be inadequate, recommendations should be made in writing in order that action may be taken to remedy the situation.

10.6 Hazard-spotting techniques

Hazard-spotting exercises are a modified version of the safety sampling method, where a particular department, hazard or work activity is singled out for a closer and more thorough examination.

The exercises should be arranged by the health and safety adviser, in conjunction with the company management, or by the training manager through line management, and should involve supervisors, safety representatives and operatives.

Observers may include first line or senior managers, but there should be at least an equal number of operatives. Some managements may prefer a predominant number of operatives up to ganger level in the team, thereby encouraging workers to take an active interest in safety and accident prevention at the workplace.

10.6.1 Hazard-spotting programme

A set and properly structured programme of inspections and sampling will ensure that all of the main activities of a firm are continuously under scrutiny. Hazard-spotting exercises should be used not only where there is seen to be a need to ensure the safety and health of people at work, but also as a preventative and continuing monitoring exercise.

10.6.2 Hazard-spotting team

Members of the proposed hazard-spotting team should have had some training or experience in health and safety matters in relation to the work or hazards to be assessed and be able to recognise any unsafe acts of people at work or unsafe or potentially unsafe conditions of work or methods of work.

One person should be appointed leader of each group, and their functions should include the following.

- ☑ The collection of the written findings of the members of the team.
- ☑ The study of these findings and the summary of unsafe acts and conditions that have been observed during the tour.
- ☑ The preparation of a brief report, setting out the unsafe acts and conditions that were observed during the tour and making recommendations for action by the management or their representative to rectify any situation that may have been observed.
- ☑ Noting and recording the response of the line or senior management, satisfying themselves that action will be taken by management to rectify any situations observed.
- ☑ Reporting back to members of the team what action will be taken by the line manager concerned.

10.6.3 Safety sampling

Health and safety sampling of a particular work activity, process or work area may be necessary in the following situations.

- ☑ The activity, process or work area presents particular health and safety concerns, where there have been changes to an activity, process or work area that are relevant to health and safety.
- ☑ There is a need to improve the health and safety performance in a particular area of operations.
- ☑ There are areas of high labour turnover.

Sampling should be carried out by someone familiar with the work activity, process or work area under inspection.

10.6.4 Safety tours

Directors, senior managers, site managers, engineers, supervisors and operatives should have the opportunity to take note of health and safety conditions prevailing within the workplace during normal construction work.

A site health and safety tour

Production, however, will often be their first priority and this need to get the job done may adversely affect their judgement on safety matters. Familiarity with certain work and hazards may further cause them to overlook, fail to recognise or ignore real or potential dangers that are present at the workplace.

For these reasons, additional **health and safety tours** (general inspections of the workplace) made by health and safety advisers, supervisors and safety representatives should take place at regular intervals.

For HSE guidance, aimed at directors and board members, covering the assessment of identifying and managing health and safety risks at work, refer to the HSE website.

10.6.5 Safety surveys

These are carried out at longer intervals to assess current safety standards and activities. They can be compared against other departments in the same organisation or similar companies within the industry.

Surveys provide the following opportunities.

- ☑ Compare the current safety performance of the company against previous years.
- ☑ Review the understanding of safety objectives and determine future objectives.
- ☑ Establish adequate and suitable current levels of safety training.
- ☑ Improve procedures, records, communication and information.
- ☑ Decide if additional resources are required.

Surveys can be anonymous to encourage an open and honest response and they can also encourage worker engagement.

10.7 Inspection reports

Details of inspections and their findings should be recorded. Commercially produced versions of inspection report forms are often multi-copy and self-duplicating, with each copy on a different coloured paper to identify the intended recipient.

Whatever the type of checklist or form used, it should provide a record of any action requested to remedy conditions and working practices considered to be unsafe. Space should be provided on the form to record the date and place of the inspection and details of any corrective action identified, subsequent action to be taken or, if no action was required, an explanation of why this was so.

Reports should also contain elements of positive or good practice, such as identifying that safe systems of work for high risk activities were being followed. Good practice should also be captured and shared and opportunities made to offer recognition to individuals who are working safely.

Remedial actions identified to eliminate or lessen the risk to health and safety should always be implemented *(refer to 10.9)*.

10.8 Audit and review

A health and safety audit is a demonstration of the management's commitment to monitor and improve, where necessary, the effectiveness of the company's safety management system from the top down.

The process of carrying out health and safety audits, evaluating the findings and implementing remedial action, where necessary, results in a continuous cycle of improvement.

Audits tend to be formal, pre-planned, events with the findings documented for later evaluation and review.

> **Audit**
>
> The structured process of collecting independent information on the efficiency, effectiveness and reliability of the total health and safety management system and identifying plans for corrective action.

Therefore, the main requirements of a health and safety audit include the following.

- ☑ A critical examination of the whole operation.
- ☑ An assessment of how the risks to health and safety are being managed.
- ☑ The identification of the efficient and safe performance of people.
- ☑ The detection and identification of falling standards, ineffective company procedures, and non-compliance with industry standards and legal requirements.
- ☑ The use of meaningful standards consistent with the organisation's operations.
- ☑ The identification and implementation of a corrective action plan.

Health and safety auditing should also be seen as an integral part of the overall monitoring of health and safety within an organisation.

The aim of such an audit is to identify problem areas that may exist, so that you can make improvements to your standard of health and safety. The audit should look at the interaction of all the activities of your company, as well as at the work itself.

Audits may discover health and safety failings that arise through factors that occur off site (such as design issues), which are therefore outside the direct control of site-based staff. They may also identify good practices that should be shared and incorporated into a process of improvement.

By comparison, health and safety inspections are normally a less formal style of audit; the results are not necessarily recorded and they may be more appropriate for some smaller sites. Remember, however, **no record – no proof!**

A health and safety inspection

Both health and safety audits and inspections are carried out on a pre-notified or no-notice basis, as suited to the situation at the time. If too many are pre-notified or regularly scheduled, it may tend to create a false impression, as those on site may only improve their behaviour or practices in the short-term.

Audits should be carried out by a member of management, often the company health and safety adviser or a director, who may or may not be accompanied by a representative(s) of sub-contractors or the employees. The aim is to identify problem areas, implement improvements and increase the overall standard of safety awareness.

It requires attention to the following.

- ☑ Work environment.
- ☑ Person carrying out the task.
- ☑ Task itself.
- ☑ Safety culture.
- ☑ Way in which each affects the others.

The important thing is that, where shortcomings are found, remedial action is promptly taken and lessons learned to prevent recurrence.

10.9 Remedial actions

A clear understanding of what remedial actions are required to eliminate or lessen the risks to health and safety, and when those actions should be taken, is an essential part of health and safety management.

The following lists suggest how shortcomings that are highlighted during health and safety inspections should be prioritised for remedial action.

10.9.1 Items requiring immediate action

- ☑ The contravention of any statutory requirements or Approved Codes of Practice.
- ☑ Any accident or incident that is reportable to the HSE under RIDDOR.
- ☑ The occurrence of accidents, incidents or near misses that produce situations of possible or immediate danger to the health and safety of employees or other people, including members of the public.
- ☑ The risk of financial liabilities, as a result of damage to plant and equipment, or compensation to workers or members of the public following litigation, the risks of fire, explosion or other hazards involving electricity, toxic materials or substances.
- ☑ The existence of unsafe working practices and unsafe places of work.
- ☑ Any activity or situation that is giving rise to conditions that could affect the short or long-term health of workers (for example, creating dust).
- ☑ Any shortages of correct and adequate personal protective clothing and equipment.
- ☑ The risk of serious environmental pollution.

10.9.2 Items requiring prompt action

- ☑ Any potential hazards that may exist, but which do not cause any imminent or immediate danger of injury, damage or pollution.
- ☑ Any signs of inadequate information, instruction or supervision, which should have been provided by either the management or others.
- ☑ Any first-aid facilities and training that fall short of statutory requirements.
- ☑ Occasions when new plant, new work methods, new equipment or different materials are to be introduced into the workplace.

10.9.3 Items requiring short-term action

- ☑ Where there is a lack of planning and control affecting safety, occupational health or the environment within the workplace, either directly or indirectly (for example through the inadequate supply of materials and equipment to enable the workforce to carry out their tasks satisfactorily and safely).
- ☑ Where there are signs of inadequacies in the personal skills, knowledge and experience of the workforce, which may have an adverse effect on safety.

10.9.4 Items requiring long-term planning and action

- Where there is a lack of certain categories of safety skills and trained personnel amongst the workforce.
- Where there is a need for the training of safety advisers, supervisors and safety representatives, to keep abreast of the future needs of the firm and its employees.
- Where there is a need for the improvement of standards of health, welfare and safety within the company.

10.10 Benchmarking

One of the most difficult things about auditing is deciding whether the measured performance is satisfactory. Within health and safety, experienced external auditors will typically audit against two parameters.

- Performance against internal systems.
- Performance against legal standards.

This is fine as it allows an organisation to self-check, but it does not indicate how a performance rates against others.

As a comparative measure, some companies use accident or injury numbers, or the number of prosecutions and/or enforcement notices.

Various attempts have been made within the industry to produce key performance indicators (KPIs) for health and safety, but difficulties are caused by comparing the relevance of, say, KPIs of a small plastering contractor employing four people to a UK Contractors Group member.

As a result there is no right or wrong answer, and it is a case of selecting areas of measurement most appropriate to a company. Another driver for benchmarking certain elements is that these may be a requirement of client or pre-qualification questionnaires. Some trade associations, including the National Access and Scaffolding Confederation (NASC), compile accident statistics for their members. The NASC believes that this covers approximately half of the scaffolding industry.

In recent years proactive indicators are measured in addition to the traditionally reactive indicators (such as accident statistics). Proactive indicators can include the number of:

- toolbox talks carried out per employee
- senior management tours
- site inspections and audits
- near-miss reports.

Benchmarking can be a very useful exercise but participants need to be aware that the information may need to be interpreted carefully.

Health and safety performance can be assessed in the following way.

- Relating it to the same reporting period of the previous year.
- Comparing it with similar organisations and/or departments in the same industry.
- Relating it to official national statistics.
- Making regional comparisons between sites in different parts of the country.

In a market of open communication between managers, such comparisons should be extremely useful and readily available to help identify and address trends, and take appropriate action where common hazards have been recognised.

A
10

10.11 Additional benefits to a company

As legislation increasingly requires risk and other assessments, contractors, principal contractors or clients are demanding sight of health and safety policies and method statements, evidence that you have an auditing programme will help your business.

A good audit will benefit everyone from senior management to the most inexperienced employee, and should be accepted on its merits as the resultant changes bring improvements in health and safety performance.

The health and safety audit should be carried out, as far as possible, by independent auditors. This overcomes the problems faced by line managers when auditing their own area of work, or even a second line manager being critical of their peers. Auditing must be carried out objectively and with a high degree of honesty when identifying non-compliance with management systems and techniques.

The frequency of safety audits should ensure that the health and safety management system of the organisation does not degrade over time or through changes in the company organisation, personnel or the work it carries out.

Several safety auditing systems are available commercially but, in the main, these are directed towards the larger business, which can afford either to employ its own dedicated auditing team or contract consultants to come in and carry out the audit.

The construction industry identified the need for an auditing system for the smaller and medium-sized company where the site manager or site supervisor could inspect the site and, within a couple of hours, produce an acceptable appreciation of the standard of safety on site.

10.12 Construction site health, safety and environment auditing system

The CITB *Construction site health, safety and environment auditing system* (SA 03 CD) is closely related to *Construction site safety* (GE 700). It is a CD-ROM containing a number of ready-made auditing forms and is aimed at companies that have not yet addressed the subject or concept of safety audits. It has been designed with simplicity in mind.

The aim is to introduce companies to safety auditing and encourage them to adopt the concept as a part of their overall safety policy. It represents a proactive, cost-effective method of becoming safer, rather than a reactive approach. It shows that the company and its staff are trying to ensure that everything is safe and prevent the conditions that cause accidents to occur, instead of picking up the pieces and changing work practices after accidents have happened.

If, in due course, it is decided that the company has outgrown this auditing system and the move is made to a more complex system, the *Construction site safety – Health, safety and environment auditing system* will have served its purpose.

If, by adopting an effective auditing system, one accident is prevented, then all the work, time and resources that a company has put into its preparation will have been worth it.

www.

For further information on the *Construction site health, safety and environment auditing system,* please contact CITB Publications or visit the website.

11

Statutory forms, notices and registers

Contents

Overview

This chapter gives a brief outline of some of the requirements for the completion and use of various statutory and non-statutory forms, notices, signs and registers used within the building and construction industry, and the keeping of some records and other details.

Some guidance on the types of daily and weekly inspection work that supervisors should carry out and records that must be kept is also included.

11.1 Introduction

Record keeping is important as it is the means used to ensure that inspections and examinations are carried out.

Some are required by legislation and others by the employer as they are good practice and vital in preventing accidents.

11.2 Important points

- ☑ The selection of the forms or notices is appropriate or applicable to the individual site or premises, and the circumstances that exist on that site.
- ☑ The listings contained in this chapter are not intended to be a full and precise guide to all the statutory requirements that currently exist. All cases of doubt should be resolved by reference to the appropriate enforcing authority or to the legislation.

A statutory inspection means legally it must be carried out.

11.3 Record keeping

Records are generally split into two categories.

Scaffold inspection with inspection tags in place

- ☑ **Proactive** (for example, inspecting scaffolding or excavations to ensure they remain safe)
- ☑ **Reactive** (for example, an accident investigation to establish the cause).

Records of toolbox talks are also important, as this demonstrates that (usually site-based) training is being provided.

Daily site briefings are a good way of reviewing what has happened and looking at what has to be done and the associated hazards for the forthcoming day. These can be extended to point of work risk assessments.

A health record must be kept for all employees under health surveillance. They must be kept for at least 40 years from the date of last entry.

Different regulations state how long inspection records should be kept. For example, the Provision and Use of Work Equipment Regulations state that an inspection record should be kept until the next inspection is made. However, inspections of excavations, cofferdams and caissons, made in accordance with the Construction (Design and Management) Regulations (CDM), have to be kept on site until the works are completed, and after that for a further three months.

An individual has three years to make a claim for neglect, act or omission where an injury or loss has been sustained.

11.4 Daily user and visual checks

Daily user and visual checks form a vital part of good site management and reduce the risk of plant and equipment breakdown or failure, such as those listed below.

- ☑ Engine or motor seizure due to lack of lubrication.
- ☑ A low-pressure tyre being damaged or causing vehicles to overturn.
- ☑ Missing scaffold edge protection causing the potential of falling materials or persons.
- ☑ Damaged power plugs, sockets and leads.

A
11

Construction plant and equipment are exposed to harsh environments and they require effective maintenance regimes to prevent defects from developing. A programme of daily visual checks, regular inspections and servicing schedules should be established according to the manufacturer's instructions and the risks associated with the use of each vehicle or tool.

Plant hire companies must provide information with all plant and equipment that they supply to enable it to be used and maintained safely. Contractual arrangements between user and hirer should set out who is responsible for maintenance and inspection during the hire period and this should be made clear to all parties.

Plant and vehicles should have a maintenance log to help manage and record maintenance operations. Employers should establish procedures designed to encourage supervisors and operators to report defects or problems, and ensure that problems with plant and vehicles are put right. Planned inspection and maintenance needs to follow manufacturers' instructions.

11.5 List of key requirements

The following is a list of key requirements. (*For an explanation of these requirements refer to Appendix A.*)

Category		Brief description
1.	**Accident book BL510 (rev 2003)**	Report of an accident must comply with the Data Protection Act.
2.	**F2508**	Report of an injury or dangerous occurrence.
3.	**F2508A**	Report of a case of disease.
4.	**F2508G1**	Report of flammable gas incidents.
5.	**F2508G2**	Report of a dangerous gas fitting.
6.	**F10**	Notification of a project.
7.	**F2067**	Ionising radiation health record.
8.	**F2533**	Safety representatives' report form.
9.	**F2534**	Safety representatives' inspection form.
10.	**Air receivers**	Safe working pressure and record of test.
11.	**Asbestos**	Licence, notice and records. Where appropriate, maintaining a written asbestos management plan.
12.	**Builders' skips**	On road, permits and signs.
13.	**Consultation with employees**	Rights of employees.
14.	**COSHH assessments**	Maintenance of assessment forms and other records.
15.	**Danger areas**	Identify with signs.
16.	**Dangerous substances and explosive atmospheres**	Display of notices.
17.	**Diving**	Records and registration.
18.	**Electrical equipment**	Records, certification of new installations.
19.	**Electric shock placard**	Display in workplaces.
20.	**Emergency evacuation**	Emergency evacuation route signage as necessary and assembly point sign(s).
21.	**Excavations, cofferdams and caissons**	Records of inspections of places of work.
22.	**Explosives**	Certificate and records.
23.	**Falsework**	Records of design, including calculations, to be kept.
24.	**Fire**	Notices for extinguishers, fire points and other fire-fighting equipment. Fire exit signs.
25.	**First aid**	Notice regarding facilities and identity of first aiders.
26.	**Food hygiene**	Display of notices, and certificates of staff training.
27.	**Fragile surfaces**	Notice to be displayed.
28.	**Hazardous substances**	Labels on containers.
29.	**Health and safety policy**	Display or distribute to all employees.

A
11

Category (continued)		Brief description
30.	Holes in floors and similar openings	Cover to be clearly marked.
31.	Information for employees (see also Training)	Display approved poster or distribute approved leaflet to all employees.
32.	Insurance (employers' liability)	Display of certificate.
33.	Ionising radiation	Advance notification to HSE of work. Licence, records and appropriate signage/ barriers at work site.
34.	Lead	Records of inspection and thorough examination of control measures.
35.	Lifting operations	Records of inspection, examination and safe working load (SWL) indication.
36.	Management of health and safety	Risk assessments, appointments, procedures.
37.	Manual handling	Assessment, marking of loads. Training.
38.	Noise	Marking of hearing protection zones.
39.	Plant and equipment	Inspection and records.
40.	Pressure vessels	Display of working pressure, and other details.
41.	Protective clothing and equipment	Assessments, maintenance, training.
42.	Safety representatives and safety committees	Access to documents, minutes, and so on. Information on identity of trade union-appointed safety reps.
43.	Safety signs	Signs and notices as appropriate.
44.	Scaffolding	Records of inspections, display of 'incomplete' notice.
45.	Training	Records.
46.	Visual display units (VDUs) or display screens	Records of assessments, training, eyesight tests.
47.	Waste management	Completion of duty of care documentation, forms, permits and certificates.
48.	Work equipment	Suitability, maintenance, warnings.
49.	Work in compressed air	Records of equipment inspection and health surveillance.
50.	Working time	Permitted hours of work.
51.	Working at height	Records of inspection of equipment.

Also refer to Section G: *Checklists and forms.*

11.6 Statutory or recommended inspections and examinations

The following table sets out the recommended daily user checks, weekly inspections, statutory inspections and examinations.

		Statutory or recommended					
Work activity plant item	**Pre-use daily**	**Weekly record**	**Monthly record**	**Three monthly record**	**Six monthly record**	**12 monthly record**	**Form for statutory examination or report to comply with**
Excavations, cofferdams and caissons	✓ Inspect	✓ Inspect					Construction (Design and Management) Regulations
Plant and equipment (not electrical or for lifting)	✓ Inspect	✓ Inspect			✓ Examine	✓ Examine	Provision and Use of Work Equipment Regulations
Plant and equipment (electrical) including RCDs	✓ Inspect	✓ Inspect		✓ Examine			Construction (Design and Management) Regulations, Electricity at Work Regulations
Cranes and plant for lifting people, MEWPs, harness, lifting accessories and safety nets	✓ Inspect	✓ Inspect			✓ Examine	✓ Examine	Provision and Use of Work Equipment Regulations, Lifting Operations and Lifting Equipment Regulations
Cranes and plant used for lifting	✓ Inspect	✓ Inspect				✓ Examine	Lifting Operations and Lifting Equipment Regulations
Work at height, all scaffolds, working platforms, mobile towers, ladders and steps, etc.	✓ Inspect	✓ Inspect					Work at Height Regulations, Provision and Use of Work Equipment Regulations, Construction (Design and Management) Regulations
Fire-fighting appliances		✓ Inspect				✓ Examine	Construction (Design and Management) Regulations, Regulatory Reform Fire Safety Order
Site offices electrical equipment and installation		✓ Inspect				✓ Examine	Construction (Design and Management) Regulations, Electricity at Work Regulations, Workplace Health Safety and Welfare Regulations

Appendix A – Brief explanation of key requirements

1.	**Accident book BL510** The keeping of an accident book is required by the Social Security (Claims and Payments) Regulations, the Social Security Administration Act and the Reporting of Injuries, Diseases and Dangerous Occurrences Regulations (RIDDOR). While there is no statutory book, the revised BL510 was produced because the previous version and other similar books did not comply with the Data Protection Act. The design of BL510 allows for an entry to be made without the personal details of a previous entry being seen. Any business that has its own accident book must ensure their version complies with the Data Protection Act. All accidents that cause any injury to an employee, no matter how slight, must be entered. Entry may be made either by the employee or anyone acting on their behalf. Completed book stubs and records must be kept for three years from the date of the last entry.
2.	**F2508 Report of an injury or dangerous occurrence** Form F2508, report of an injury or dangerous occurrence, is required by the Reporting of Injuries, Diseases and Dangerous Occurrences Regulations (RIDDOR). Notification should now be made online. The form will then be submitted directly to the RIDDOR database and a copy received back for record purposes. All incidents can be reported online but a telephone service remains for reporting fatal and specified injuries only.
3.	**F2508A Report of a case of disease** A report on form F2508A is required by the Reporting of Injuries, Diseases and Dangerous Occurrences Regulations (RIDDOR). It must be completed when a registered medical practitioner has diagnosed in writing that an employee is suffering from a scheduled reportable disease and the person has been employed in a scheduled work activity by the employer.
4.	**F2508G1 Report of flammable gas incidents** A report is required online, via this form, if you are a distributor, filler, importer or supplier of flammable gas and you learn, either directly or indirectly, that someone has died or suffered a specified injury in connection with the gas that you distributed, filled, imported or supplied.
5.	**F2508G2 Report of a dangerous gas fitting** Gas installation businesses, registered with the Gas Safe register, must provide the HSE with details (using this form) of any gas appliances or fittings that they consider to be dangerous to such an extent that people could die or suffer specified injuries because the design, construction, installation, modification or servicing could result in: ■ an accidental leakage of gas ■ inadequate combustion of gas (such as increasing the proportion of carbon monoxide in appliance flue gases to a dangerously high level in normal or abnormal and adverse weather conditions) ■ inadequate removal of the gas combustion products.
6.	**F10 Notification of a project under the Construction (Design and Management) Regulations** This form is required under the above regulations and may be filled out and submitted to the HSE online before the start of any construction work on a construction site. A project is notifiable if the construction work is likely to: ■ last for more than 30 working days and have more than 20 workers working simultaneously at any point in the project, or ■ exceed 500 person days.
7.	**F2067 Ionising radiation health record** The record, or a copy of it, must be preserved until the person to whom it relates has or would have attained the age of 75 years, but in any event for at least 50 years from the date of the last entry.
8.	**F2533 Safety representatives' report form** The Safety Representatives and Safety Committees Regulations This form is used by trade union-appointed safety representatives to notify the employer of any matter discovered during a workplace inspection, which is considered to be unsafe and/or unhealthy.
9.	**F2534 Safety representatives' inspection form** This form is used by trade union-appointed safety representatives to record the time, date and location of workplace health and safety inspections carried out.
10.	**Air receivers** The Pressure Systems Safety Regulations Every air receiver must have the safe working pressure clearly displayed on it. It must be examined and tested as laid down in the regulations and records kept.

11.	**Asbestos** The Control of Asbestos Regulations Virtually all work with asbestos requires a licence from the HSE or the giving of 14-days' notice of the intention to work with asbestos to the enforcing authority. The majority of work must only be undertaken by a licensed contractor. This work includes most asbestos removal, all work with sprayed asbestos coatings and asbestos lagging and most work with asbestos insulation and asbestos insulating board (AIB). Brief written records should be kept of non-licensed work, which has to be notified (for example, copy of the notification with a list of workers on the job), plus the level of likely exposure of those workers to asbestos. This does not require air monitoring on every job if an estimate of degree of exposure can be made, based on experience of similar past tasks or published guidance. Persons in charge of premises have a duty to manage the existence of asbestos in those premises, which will entail keeping records of surveys and possibly a register of where asbestos has been found, its condition and how its presence is being managed. This is known as an asbestos management plan. If an employee is exposed to asbestos above the control limit, health records of the employee must be maintained and kept for 40 years after the date of the last entry. All products containing asbestos must be properly labelled. All waste must be in properly sealed and labelled containers.
12.	**Builders' skips** The Highways Act – Section 139 If a builder's skip is placed on a road, a permit must be obtained from the local highway authority and the requirements of the permit strictly followed. These will include ensuring the skip is properly lit during the hours of darkness. It must not pose a hazard to highway users and pedestrians and be clearly and indelibly marked with the owner's name and telephone number or address.
13.	**Consultation with employees** The Health and Safety (Consultation with Employees) Regulations were introduced because the Health and Safety at Work Act 1974 only covered union-appointed safety representatives. They now extend to all employees the right to have consultation with their employers and be provided with information. There are many similarities with the Safety Representative and Safety Committee Regulations and they also implement the consultation provisions of the European Union Framework Directive on health and safety.
14.	**Control of Substances Hazardous to Health and Approved Code of Practice** The Control of Substances Hazardous to Health Regulations (COSHH) and the Approved Code of Practice (ACoP) require assessments to be made of substances hazardous to health and, except in the simplest and most obvious of cases, for the assessments to be written and kept accessible for those who need to know the results. If health surveillance is appropriate, the health records of employees under health surveillance must be maintained and kept for 40 years after the date of the last entry. All mechanical control measures (such as dust extraction) must be subject to routine examination in accordance with the regulations and records kept. Substances hazardous to health must be properly labelled.
15.	**Danger areas** Identify with signs under the Work at Height Regulations.
16.	**Dangerous substances and explosive atmospheres** Under the Dangerous Substances and Explosive Atmospheres Regulations, the following definitions and conditions apply. **Dangerous substances** A substance or preparation that is explosive, oxidising, extremely flammable, highly flammable or flammable, or any dust that can form an explosive mixture with air or an explosive atmosphere. **Explosive atmosphere** A mixture, under atmospheric conditions, of air and one or more dangerous substance in the form of gases, vapours, mists or dusts in which, after ignition has occurred, combustion spreads to the entire unburned mixture. Where an explosive atmosphere may occur, a specific sign is to be erected. In accordance with the Health and Safety (Safety Signs and Signals) Regulations, the sign must consist of black letters on a triangular yellow background with black edging.
17.	**Diving** The Diving Operations at Work Regulations Records have to be kept of the written appointment of all diving supervisors and of the qualifications and medical certificates of divers. All dives have to be recorded in the diver's logbook. Diving rules have to be in writing. Diving is a very specialised area, even in onshore waters. All diving contractors must be registered with the HSE.
18.	**Electrical equipment** The Electricity at Work Regulations All electrical equipment, including portable equipment, should be inspected on a regular basis by a competent person and records kept. Portable electric tools should be PAT-tested in accordance with HSE guidance.

19.	**Electric shock placard** The Electricity at Work Regulations Guidance notices or placards giving details of emergency resuscitation procedures in the event of an electric shock should be displayed in locations where people are at an enhanced risk of electric shock.
20.	**Emergency evacuation** The Construction (Design and Management) Regulations state there must be a sufficient number of emergency escape routes, which must lead as directly as possible to a point of safety. Escape routes must be indicated by signs and kept clear and free from obstructions.
21.	**Excavations, cofferdams and caissons** The Construction (Design and Management) Regulations require that excavations, cofferdams and caissons must be inspected and written reports of the inspections made.
22.	**Explosives** Virtually all possession of explosives requires an explosives certificate, which is issued by the local chief officer of police. Detailed records have to be kept of all movements or usages of explosives.
23.	**Falsework and temporary works** The Construction (Design and Management) Regulations and British Standard BS 5975 *Code of Practice for Falsework* These regulations include falsework under the definition of construction work and, therefore, the designer's duties apply. Temporary works require designing and can simply be defined as anything that is not part of the permanent works. It is recommended that records should be kept of all design calculations, drawings, estimated loadings and specifications for falsework, together with written permissions to pour concrete or to load falsework, and to dismantle it.
24.	**Fire** The Regulatory Reform (Fire Safety) Order The requirement for fire certificates is now discontinued. Documentary information relating to fire safety should include: ■ records of staff training in the use of extinguishers ■ records of fire extinguisher servicing ■ records of practice evacuations ■ written fire risk assessment and a written fire safety plan ■ display of relevant signs where flammable and highly flammable substances are stored.
25.	**First aid** The Health and Safety (First Aid) Regulations states: **'An employer shall inform his employees of the arrangements that have been made in connection with the provision of first aid, including the location of equipment, facilities and personnel.'** The guidance notes recommend that first-aid notices are displayed as an effective means of informing the workforce of the employer's arrangement for first aid. There is no statutory form but a range of first-aid notices are available from the suppliers of workplace safety signs.
26.	**Food hygiene** The Food Safety Act Toilets adjacent to food rooms must be separated by a lobby. A notice stating 'Now wash your hands' must be displayed. Checks and inspections of equipment and staff training should be recorded. Certificates of staff training in food hygiene and handling must be displayed.
27.	**Fragile surfaces** A requirement of the Work at Height Regulations is that if people have to work near or pass close by any fragile roofing materials, the appropriate warning notices must be clearly displayed at all approaches to the area.
28.	**Hazardous substances** Generally, under the Control of Substances Hazardous to Health Regulations and the European Union Directive for Classification, Packaging and Labelling of Dangerous Goods, all containers containing hazardous substances should be clearly marked with their contents and the appropriate hazard warning symbol. Assessments must be made and, with minor exceptions, recorded. (There is no statutory form.) (*See also entries under **Asbestos** and **Lead**.*)
29.	**Health and safety policy** The Health and Safety at Work Act 1974 requires employers to have a safety policy and arrangements to bring it into force. If more than five persons are employed, that policy must be written down. There is no statutory form but the HSE publication *Writing your health* and *safety policy statement* may be used. The policy must be brought to the notice of all employees.

30.	**Holes in floors and similar openings** The Work at Height Regulations require that holes in floors and flat roofs, where a person is liable to fall through (referred to as danger areas in the regulations), must be properly protected. If a cover is used over a hole it must be clearly marked to show its purpose.
31.	**Information for employees** The Health and Safety (Information for Employees) Regulations requires every employer to display the approved health and safety law poster in a position where it can be easily read by the employees, or to give to each employee a copy of the approved leaflet entitled *Health and safety law. What you should know,* which contains the same information.
32.	**Insurance (employers' liability)** The Employers' Liability (Compulsory Insurance) Act requires there to be in force insurance against liability for bodily injury or disease sustained by employees. The Employers' Liability (Compulsory Insurance) Regulations require a certificate of employers' liability insurance to be displayed at the place of business in such a position that it can be easily seen and read by employees, including every construction site. Employers can display an online version of the certificate, providing all employees have access to it. A hard copy may still be displayed.
33.	**Ionising radiation** Under the provisions of the Ionising Radiation Regulations, any employer intending to use any source of ionising radiation must give 28-days' notice to the HSE. Very detailed records, including health records, have to be kept. Advice should be sought from the HSE or other competent source. The appropriate warning signs and notices for controlled areas must be displayed.
34.	**Lead** The Control of Lead at Work Regulations together with the Approved Code of Practice and guidance notes require a number of forms to be completed by employers (and in some cases medical practitioners) if the required risk assessment under the regulations carried out by the employer shows that an employee's exposure to lead is liable to be significant. Some of the types of work likely to lead to significant exposure are: ■ high temperature work (over 500°C), including welding and cutting ■ abrasion of lead or lead-painted surfaces ■ spray painting with lead paint. Details of all the forms are given in the Approved Code of Practice.
35.	**Lifting operations** Under the Lifting Operations and Lifting Equipment Regulations: ■ all machinery and accessories used for lifting are marked to indicate their safe working load (SWL) for each configuration in which they can be used ■ lifting equipment designed to lift persons is clearly marked as such ■ lifting equipment not designed for lifting persons but which could be easily mistaken for such is marked appropriately ■ all lifting equipment and accessories are subjected to a scheme of thorough examination ■ records of thorough examination are made and kept available for inspection.
36.	**Management of health and safety** There is no statutory or recommended style of form for risk, or any other assessments. Your own devised form or a commercially obtained form may be completed either manually or on a computer database. Risk assessments must be made of all work activities. **If you employ five or more people, the significant findings must be recorded and, in addition:** ■ health surveillance – if needed, individual health records must be kept ■ emergency procedures – must be written down.
37.	**Manual handling** The Manual Handling Operations Regulations Assessment to be made where risks from manual handling cannot be avoided. It is recommended that all but the simplest assessments should be recorded.
38.	**Noise** The Control of Noise at Work Regulations requires that all hearing protection zones are identified by means of a sign (see the Health and Safety (Safety Signs and Signals) Regulations). A hearing protection zone is anywhere where an employee is likely to be exposed to a daily personal noise exposure of 85 dB(A) or a peak sound pressure of 137 dB(C).
39.	**Plant and equipment** If it is not otherwise provided for, it is strongly recommended that all plant, tools and equipment are subject to inspection and examination, and proper records kept. This will fulfil the employer's obligations under the Health and Safety at Work Act 1974, Section 2 and the Provision and Use of Work Equipment Regulations. A daily inspection and a six-monthly examination may be appropriate. Insurance companies may also require such routine inspections and examinations.

40.	**Pressure vessels** The Simple Pressure Vessels (Safety) Regulations apply to all pressure vessels intended to contain air or nitrogen at a greater pressure than 0.5 bar. Any such vessel first used after 1 July 1992 must have (amongst other things) details of the maximum working pressure, maximum and minimum working temperatures, and cubic capacity clearly displayed on it.
41.	**Protective clothing and equipment** The Personal Protective Equipment at Work Regulations The following must be recorded: ▪ risk assessment of the need for personal protective equipment (PPE) ▪ PPE inspection, maintenance or results of any required tests ▪ records of PPE issue and use.
42.	**Safety representatives and safety committees** The Safety Representative and Safety Committees Regulations, and the Approved Code of Practice and guidance notes, give safety representatives the right to inspect and take copies of any document relevant to safety that an employer is required to keep (except health records of identifiable individuals). The employer must make available to them any health and safety information that would help safety representatives fulfil their functions. Where a safety committee has been established, proper minutes and records should be kept. Safety representatives may give written reports to management concerning safety in the workplace.
43.	**Safety signs** The Health and Safety (Safety Signs and Signals) Regulations All signs giving health or safety information or instructions must comply with the relevant British Standard. A safety sign is anything that combines geometrical shape, colour and pictorial symbols to give safety information.
44.	**Scaffolding** ▪ Display of incomplete scaffold notice. Under the Work at Height Regulations, designated danger areas must be created where there is a risk of a person falling or being hit by a falling object. In the case of incomplete scaffolding, suitable notices must be displayed to discourage attempted access on to the scaffold. ▪ Handover certificates. There are no statutory provisions requiring the use or production of scaffold handover certificates. However, all reputable scaffold contractors will issue them and they can be used to demonstrate that the scaffold was properly erected by competent persons and for the purpose for which the scaffold was designed. ▪ Reports of inspections. To be completed and retained to comply with the Work at Height Regulations.
45.	**Training** Generally, Section 2 of the Health and Safety at Work Act 1974, together with various other regulations made under the principal Act, require employers to provide information, instruction and training. It is most strongly recommended that all such information, instruction and training are properly and fully recorded so that employers are in a position to prove that duties under the Act or regulations have been met.
46.	**Visual display units (VDUs) or display screens** The Health and Safety (Display Screen Equipment) Regulations Suitable and sufficient analysis of workstations for the purpose of assessing health and safety risks. All but the simplest and obvious cases must be recorded. Entitles employees to eyesight tests. Records of requests and results are recommended.
47.	**Waste management** All contractors that carry or collect waste should have a waste carrier's licence and all waste disposal facilities should have a waste management licence or permit unless they are exempt. All waste transfers must be supported by the correct documentation, called a controlled waste transfer note; or in the case of hazardous waste, a consignment note.
48.	**Work equipment** The Provision and Use of Work Equipment Regulations Records must be kept, including risk assessment for selection and use, regular and statutory inspections, maintenance, training and instructions. All work equipment must be marked in a clearly visible manner where necessary, in the interests of health and safety. Warnings, audible or visible, to be incorporated into work equipment as necessary.

49.	**Work in compressed air** The Work in Compressed Air Regulations This is an extremely specialist area where expert knowledge is needed. Detailed records are required to be kept of such areas, as: ■ clinical by a doctor ■ exposure by a compressed air contractor ■ health by an employer. These records need maintaining for 40 years from the date of the last entry.
50.	**Working time** The Working Time Regulations give details of permitted work hours and special consideration that should be given to young workers. Records of agreements, which can only last up to five years, must be kept by the employer.
51.	**Working at height** The Work at Height Regulations This regulation specifies the need for competence in all persons involved in any capacity with regard to work at height. Any training carried out to achieve competency should be recorded. Where any person at work may pass across or near to a fragile surface, or actually work on it, prominent signs indicating that it is a fragile surface must be fixed at every approach to that place. Where any person could be injured by falling or being hit by a falling object, danger areas must be created to prevent such an occurrence. Danger areas must be clearly indicated, usually by signs and/or barriers. Where inspections of work equipment are carried out under this regulation, a record of the inspection must be made and retained as specified.

A
11

12

Accident prevention and control

Contents

Supporting information

G: Checklists and forms

GT 700 Toolbox talks

Overview

There are many factors to understand as to why accidents happen in construction, the trends and causes, the impact they can have and the preventative measures that are required. By reading this chapter managers should gain an appreciation of what factors need to be considered when developing construction phase plans, safe systems of work, assessing risk, undertaking site inspections and managing health and safety on site on a day-to-day basis.

12.1 Introduction

Accident statistics are a reliable indicator of the health and safety performance of the construction industry. The Health and Safety Executive (HSE) publishes an annual statistical report of the accidents, fatalities and occupational diseases across all industries.

This report, which is useful because it highlights accident trends, is freely downloadable from the HSE website.

On average, there are 46 annual construction fatalities. The construction industry statistics for 2013-14 are given below.

- There were 42 construction fatalities. 14 of these were to the self-employed.
- There were an estimated 76,000 total cases of work-related ill health, of which 31,000 were new cases.
- There were 1,900 reported specified injuries, compared with an average of 2,456 over the previous five years.
- There were 3,293 reported over seven-day injuries, compared with 3,213 in the previous five years.
- Falls from height are the biggest cause of fatalities. 19 people died falling from height and 581 reported fall from height specified injuries.
- Manual handling accounts for 30% of all reported over seven-day injuries.
- Slips and trips account for 22% of all reported over three-day injuries.
- An estimated 2.3 million working days were lost due to workplace ill health and a further 592,000 due to workplace injuries, making a total of 1.1 days lost per worker.
- Injuries and new cases of ill health from current construction working conditions cost society over £1.1 billion each year.
- Vibration white finger, carpal tunnel syndrome, occupational deafness and dermatitis are the most common cases of non-lung disease in the construction industry.

For an extract from the HSE's health and safety statistics for 2013-14 detailing the kinds of injuries in construction refer to Appendix A.

Each year the plan of work for the construction division of the HSE acknowledges that some parts of the industry have made significant steps forward over recent years; this is particularly noticeable on larger projects. However, these improvements are not mirrored to anything like the same extent on smaller sites, where many instances of unacceptable standards can still be found.

For details of the HSE's plan of work refer to the GE 700 *Supporting information* book.

A
12

The industry is starting to experience a culture change so that health and safety is not only about the tangible things, like wearing mandatory personal protective equipment (PPE), pedestrian segregation or providing collective fall prevention, but also about issues such as **worker engagement** and an openness and honesty from both management and the workforce to ensure that work is organised and carried out safely.

This diagram is a version of **Bird's triangle**. Its aim is to simply demonstrate the approximate relationships between the different levels of accident that occur. The triangle shows that for each fatality there are 10 serious injuries, 30 accidents with injury, 600 incidents without injury (near misses or property/equipment/ material damage) and thousands of unsafe acts or conditions.

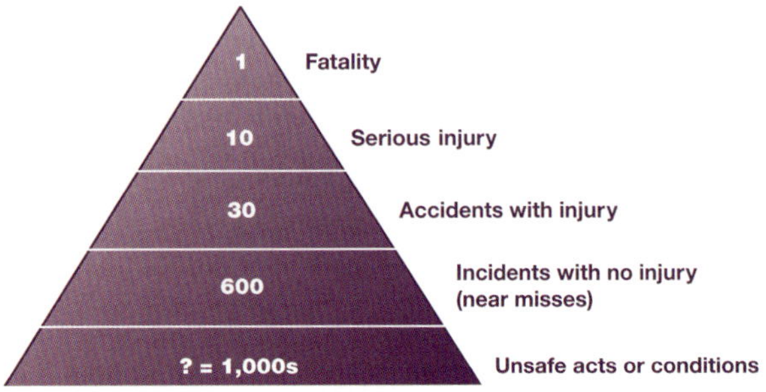

Bird's accident triangle

Bird's research illustrates that accident prevention should not be about just concentrating on fatalities and serious injury, but on preventing unsafe acts and conditions. Near misses can be an early indication that unsafe acts or conditions are happening, rather than reacting to actual accident and injury trends. This is why near-miss reporting and proactive hazard-spotting techniques (such as pre-use daily checks, workplace inspections and audits) are so important.

An unsafe act or near miss under a slightly different set of circumstances could be a serious or even fatal accident. This makes accident prevention more difficult, particularly if the incidents go unreported.

Many companies have found that their accident rate has reduced as the number of reported incidents with no injury or near misses has increased through management encouragement for such incidents to be reported.

12.2 Important points

- ☑ The construction industry remains a high risk industry and consistently accounts for a high number of fatalities and accidents.
- ☑ The construction industry accounts for about 5% of employees in Great Britain, but it accounts for 31% of fatal injuries and 10% of specified injuries.
- ☑ Accident prevention has to be actively managed; a good safety record will not just happen and everyone on site has their part to play.
- ☑ Reported details of accidents show that in the vast majority of cases the accident could easily have been prevented by taking simple precautions.
- ☑ The HSE has stated that many accidents result from decisions taken before work actually starts (planning and identifying safe systems of work).
- ☑ You may have no influence over these decisions but find that you need to challenge the health and safety implications that arise as a consequence of them.
- ☑ The true cost of an accident goes beyond the financial implications.
- ☑ Statistics show that new starters on site, and those at both ends of the age spectrum, are the most prone to accidents.

Accident prevention

- ☑ There are many interpretations of the word *accident*, but it is generally agreed that an **accident** is an unplanned, unscheduled, unwanted event or occurrence, or any undesired circumstance, that may result in injury to persons and damage to property. The injured person may not be an employee and property may not belong to an employer.
- ☑ **Hazard** is the potential to cause harm, including ill health and injury; damage to property, plant products or environment; production losses or liabilities.
- ☑ **Risk** is the likelihood that a specified, undesired event will occur due to the realisation of a hazard by or during work or by products created by work.
- ☑ An alternative word that is sometimes used for an accident is **incident**. The main difference in the use of this word is that an incident is something that happened, which may or may not have resulted in an injury or damage.

12.3 Near-miss reporting

The importance of learning from experience cannot be overstated. It is an essential element of accident prevention. A near miss is an incident that had the potential to result in personal injury and/or damage to the structure under construction, plant and equipment or the environment. Individual companies will decide on their criteria for categorising an incident as a near miss.

Unsafe conditions

Something with the potential to cause harm

Near misses

An incident that nearly resulted in an injury or damage

Accidents

An incident that resulted in an injury or damage

The details of all near misses must be accurately and honestly reported to enable the circumstances to be investigated and measures put in place to prevent a recurrence. In many cases, the only person able to give a full and accurate account of what happened will be the person who got it wrong.

To achieve an effective reporting system, the following are required of the workforce.

- ☑ To trust that management will treat the incident fairly and objectively.
- ☑ Be encouraged to report near misses with the assurance that individuals involved will not be disadvantaged by their honesty.
- ☑ Have confidence that the issues raised will be addressed, or else 'why bother?'.
- ☑ Be provided with the means of promptly recording the details of exactly what happened and offering their opinion as to why it occurred.

Companies may find it is beneficial to provide easy to access near-miss reporting forms, which can be completed in privacy and anonymously if that is the individual's choice. However, anonymous reporting does not provide the opportunity for follow-up discussions to establish more details, and it may encourage malicious reports to be submitted.

Evidence shows that near-miss reporting linked to recognition or a reward scheme has the best chance of succeeding.

For an example of a near miss report form refer to Section G: *Checklists and forms*.

12.4 Accident and incident trends

Broad categories are used to classify all accidents that are reported to the HSE. Each year the HSE publishes the reportable accident statistics for the previous year. This enables year-on-year trends to be established.

Reportable accident statistics for the construction industry show that the same types of accident figure prominently in the statistics year after year. Falls from height, manual handling injuries, being struck by a moving object (often plant) and slips and trips continue to figure prominently.

Now that the construction industry's output has slowed, further challenges may have been added as the competition for contracts has increased and tendered margins decreased. Commercial pressure may tempt contractors to take increased risks with their employees' health and/or safety.

The stubborn resistance of the accident statistics to significantly reduce is often attributed to the difficult working conditions experienced on construction sites, where the environment of the workplace is continually changing as work progresses. However, in reality it is often due to a lack of training or health and safety awareness among construction workers, or a lack of effective health and safety management. Current accident statistics for the construction industry indicate that about 14 people suffer a specified injury every working day and four people are killed every month.

12.5 The cost of accidents and incidents

12.5.1 Cost to the victim and their family

- ☑ Pain and suffering.
- ☑ Loss of earnings.
- ☑ Extra expense.
- ☑ Continuing disability and depression.
- ☑ Incapacity for the same job.
- ☑ Incapacity for work outside the job.
- ☑ Effect on dependants and friends.

12.5.2 Cost to people directly responsible

- ☑ Worry and stress.
- ☑ Recriminations and guilt.
- ☑ Extra work (reports, training and recruitment).
- ☑ Loss of credibility.

12.5.3 Cost to the company

- ☑ Working time lost by victim.
- ☑ Time lost by other employees out of sympathy, curiosity or discussion.
- ☑ Time lost by supervisors and others investigating the accident.
- ☑ Possible damage to machines or materials.
- ☑ Idle time (replan, repair and reinstate job).
- ☑ Rise in insurance premiums and cost of prosecution or civil action.
- ☑ Damage to reputation and possible failure to obtain work.

12.5.4 Cost to the working group

- Shock, disbelief, anger and personal grief.
- Low morale and effects on production.

12.5.5 Cost to the nation

In social and economic terms, accidents are an unwanted expense.

- Hundreds of thousands of person-days are lost each year.
- Industrial accidents have an impact on NHS resources.
- Millions of pounds are paid in pensions and death benefits.
- Countless lives are changed for the worse.

Whilst there can be no complete end cost figure, the size of the problem can be seen to be huge. Therefore anything that helps to reduce the number of accidents must benefit both the nation and the individuals concerned.

It must be stressed that these are all negative impacts. Good health and safety management prevents accidents, which means less or no victims or affected families, no additional costs to companies, no loss of reputation and no loss of work.

12.6 HSE research into accident costs

www.

HSE Research Report No. 464 contains a number of accident case studies that highlight the cost of accidents to the victims, in the widest terms.

Several of the case studies feature accidents to construction workers. The consequences of each accident are considered from different standpoints.

- **Vocational** – future job prospects.
- **Financial** – loss of earnings and future earnings.
- **Social** – standard-of-life issue for victim and family.
- **Behavioural** – reliance on medication, inability to concentrate, inability to sleep, ill-temper, and so on.
- **Psychological** – mood swings, loss of memory, emotional instability and guilt.

Examples of the impact that the accidents had on the victims, as extracted from the construction case studies, are listed below.

- 'I had no realistic prospect of returning to work in the immediate future'.
- 'I received no support from company or colleagues upon returning to work other than 'light duties' for the first two weeks'.
- 'My family was reliant on state benefits of £66 per week during three and a half months off work'.
- 'I am unable to bathe or dress myself, have problems with walking and no longer visit the gym'.
- 'I am unable to sleep due to discomfort, increased eating and inability to concentrate'.
- 'Years later I still suffer flashbacks and nightmares'.

12.7 Causes of accidents and incidents

Examining accident details will help to establish common factors and trends, revealing any weaknesses in a company's health and safety management system. Accidents can be caused by the unsafe acts and attitudes of people at work, which result in unsafe conditions being created. They are also caused by a lack of foresight or planning, which may be a failure to set up a safe system of work, or failure to appreciate the results of risk assessments, COSHH assessments or other similar work.

Unsafe acts can create unsafe conditions, which can cause accidents. These accidents often result in injury or damage.

It is impossible to list all the different types of unsafe acts and unsafe conditions that can exist in the construction industry. However, it is worth recording those that have been the most frequent known causes of accidents on construction sites. These have resulted from the following.

- ☑ Lack of planning, management control and supervision.
- ☑ Lack of knowledge of good safety techniques or lack of safety awareness.
- ☑ Unsafe methods of working at height, including lack of provision for fall prevention.
- ☑ Incorrect use of machinery and equipment.
- ☑ Failure to segregate operating plant and pedestrians.
- ☑ Failure to inspect and maintain all types of machinery and equipment.
- ☑ Incorrect use of tools and equipment (hand tools and power tools).
- ☑ Use of faulty equipment with improvised repairs or modifications.
- ☑ Unsafe manual handling (lifting, loading, moving, stacking, storing).
- ☑ Overloading of working places (scaffolds, false work, hoists, machines, vehicles, roofs).
- ☑ Failure to use protective safety equipment (helmets, goggles, gloves, masks, footwear).
- ☑ Carrying out work on moving parts with guards removed or safety devices inoperative.
- ☑ Failure to report faulty or unsafe equipment, or dangerous occurrences and incidents.
- ☑ Creating unstable structures.

12.8 Planning for health and safety

Despite the effort made by the majority to fulfil their legal, moral and social obligations, difficulties are often encountered in human behaviour that require time and tolerance before acceptable safety standards are achieved.

It is essential that careful consideration is given to pre-planning, communication, training, supervision and the dissemination of information, if safe systems and places of work are to be developed and maintained.

All of the following measures can make a significant contribution towards the prevention of accidents through the implementation of safe systems of work and procedures.

- ☑ Allowing enough money and time to do the work safely.
- ☑ Providing adequate protection and guarding of working places, platforms, machinery, tools, plant and equipment.
- ☑ Implementing an adequate system for the maintenance and repair of plant, equipment and tools.
- ☑ Providing appropriate training, instruction and information at all levels, including safety training.
- ☑ Providing adequate supervision and control.
- ☑ Planning, siting and/or stacking materials and equipment to allow safe access or egress of site plant, vehicles and equipment.
- ☑ Pre-planning and organising site layout, to provide maximum efficiency, safety and progression of the work sequences and operations.
- ☑ Providing adequate resources and equipment to protect and maintain the health and welfare of all personnel.
- ☑ Producing, declaring, maintaining and supporting a safety policy, and updating it as appropriate to accommodate advancement and development.
- ☑ Bringing about and maintaining an awareness of, and compliance with, all safety legislation and information relating to systems and procedures of work.

The safe separation of construction plant and pedestrians avoids accidents

12.9 Factors to consider

Health and safety at work will be affected by human and personal factors, job factors and environmental factors.

12.9.1 Human and personal factors

Attitudes of people at work often play an important part in the prevention of accidents, and conversely, a wrong attitude can cause accidents to happen. Attitudes differ depending on the characteristics of the person.

- ☑ Age and sex.
- ☑ General health, natural dexterity, agility, physique and ability.
- ☑ Disabilities, if any.
- ☑ Senses of smell, sight, hearing, touch and, sometimes, taste.
- ☑ Education and qualifications, training and skills.
- ☑ Home and social life, status at home and work and position in peer group.

Safe attitudes = safe actions = safe conditions.

For further information refer to the HSE publication *Reducing error and influencing behaviour.*

12.9.2 Job factors

Every work activity has a degree of inherent hazard. Building and construction sites can be particularly hazardous and demand the co-ordination of a large number of trades, skills and work at any one time.

Particular attention should be given to the following.

- ☑ The adequacy of time and resources to plan the job and to do the job.
- ☑ Provision of tools and equipment that are safe to use and properly maintained.
- ☑ Implementation of safe systems of work.
- ☑ Personnel who are unfamiliar with established safe systems of work and practices.
- ☑ Personnel who are new to a specific worksite or unfamiliar with a new working environment.
- ☑ Those lacking induction training and/or experience.
- ☑ The provision of adequate training, information and supervision.
- ☑ Balanced workload, fatigue and boredom.

12.9.3 Environmental factors

The majority of people do not work in isolation. The attitudes of others in a working group (for example, managers, supervisors, safety officers, safety representatives and shop stewards) may help to prevent accidents, but the following should also be considered.

- ☑ The accident record of the firm, site and working group.
- ☑ The inter-relationship of people within the group.
- ☑ Information and communication processing methods.
- ☑ Weather conditions (hot, cold, wet, wind, ice or snow).
- ☑ Working at heights, in confined spaces or underground.
- ☑ Working conditions (noise, dust, light and ventilation).
- ☑ Health and welfare facilities.

12.10 Hazards

12.10.1 Obvious dangers

- ☑ Vehicles not being segregated from pedestrians.
- ☑ The presence of highly flammable material and other fire hazards.
- ☑ Work platforms or work places at height with no fall prevention.
- ☑ Insecurely stacked, slung, lifted and transported loads.
- ☑ Unsafe machinery, equipment and tools.
- ☑ Unsafe working areas due to weather conditions.
- ☑ Confined spaces or unsupported excavations.

12.10.2 Potentially dangerous situations

Below are examples of circumstances that might result in an accident.

- ☑ Working with machinery or tools with guards or fences removed.
- ☑ Using the incorrect type of plant, tools or equipment for the work involved.
- ☑ Unauthorised removal of guard-rails, or failure to replace them following removal for access of plant or materials.
- ☑ Transport of insecure or unstable loads.
- ☑ Dropping tools and materials from a height.
- ☑ Failure to wear PPE.
- ☑ Working in unstable excavations, without adequate supervision and control.
- ☑ Untidy working places or congested walkways and areas, creating a tripping hazard.
- ☑ Working at height or over water without edge and/or personal protection.
- ☑ Inadequate, incorrect or badly placed lighting.
- ☑ Unsafe electrical equipment, underground services and overhead cables.

12.10.3 Operational risks

Examples of work requiring competence, careful monitoring and/or close supervision are listed below.

High risk activities	Operations creating health hazards or risk of injury
■ Demolition ■ Working at height ■ Excavations ■ Lifting operations ■ Work in confined spaces ■ Timber, concrete or steel frame erection ■ Roof work and cladding ■ Work associated with live traffic	■ Work producing dust or fumes ■ Jobs with continual high exposure to noise or vibration ■ Jobs with continuous elements of the same type of manual handling (such as block laying and kerb laying) ■ Work with asbestos ■ Work with hazardous substances (respiratory, eye splash and skin)

12.10.4 Site security

Owners or occupiers of sites have a civil duty to protect the health and safety of **anyone** who might enter the site, even if that entry is unlawful. This duty is also stipulated in the CDM Regulations and the contractor or, where applicable, the principal contractor must take the necessary steps to prevent unauthorised access to site. Contractors must not commence work until reasonable steps have been taken to prevent unauthorised access. This includes members of the public, particularly young children (who in some cases have been killed or injured), who may trespass on the site, either during or outside of normal working hours.

These include accidents from falls into holes, being trapped by earth, or drowning, accidents involving vehicles and those involving falls and falling materials.

In all these cases, better site security and management might have prevented the accident. Contractors must take all reasonable and practical steps to ensure that sites are secure.

www.

For further information refer to the HSE publication *Protecting the public: your next move.*

The guidance focuses on the reality that hazardous construction work can be a fatal danger, not only for those within the industry but for the wider public too.

Site security

A house builder repeatedly ignored warnings to fence off a potentially dangerous construction site and was subsequently given a two year conditional discharge. They were ordered to pay £859.85 in costs and a victim surcharge of £15 after pleading guilty to a single breach of Section 27(s) of the Construction (Design and Management) Regulations.

12.11 Implications of inexperience

12.11.1 Young persons

A young person is anyone under the age of 18.

Before employing a young person, the employer must assess the risks to the young person's health and safety arising from the work they are required to do, in accordance with the regulations. This assessment must take account of a number of factors.

- The inexperience and immaturity of young persons, and their lack of awareness of risks.
- The type of any work equipment involved and the way it is used.
- The potential for exposure to physical, biological and chemical agents.
- Any health and safety training that is required for young persons.

Having carried out this assessment, employers must then determine whether the level of risk has been reduced to as low as is reasonably practicable. There is particular importance placed on avoiding work that:

- is beyond the young person's physical or psychological capacity
- involves harmful exposure to agents that are toxic or carcinogenic, causes heritable genetic damage or harm to an unborn child or which in any way chronically affects human health
- involves harmful exposure to radiation
- involves the risk of accident, which it may be reasonably assumed cannot be recognised by young people owing to their insufficient attention to safety or lack of experience or training
- involves exposure to physical agents (such as extreme cold or heat, noise and vibration).

Consideration to the level of acceptable risk may be given for young persons over the minimum school-leaving age, where the work is necessary for their training, and where they are properly supervised.

12.11.2 New starters

New starters in a company or on a site and inexperienced persons of any age have similar problems to those of young workers.

They are subjected to a new environment, rules, methods and procedures; are under different supervision; and are working with new colleagues using a variety of tools, equipment and manual effort to produce the work required. The start of their health and safety training is usually an induction into the company.

The need for refresher and continuance training should be reviewed at intervals and carried out as necessary.

12.11.3 Older workers

Quite correctly there is legislation in place that makes it illegal to discriminate against older workers. It is also interesting, however, to note that the number of incidents to older workers is higher than average. There are various reasons that have been suggested as to why.

- Overfamiliarity with the job.
- General slowing of reactions.
- General loss of strength and flexibility.
- Pre-existing damage to body and systems.
- Age-related degeneration of hearing and eyesight.

What is also noteworthy is that when an older person is injured, often the recovery time is longer, because the injury is more severe than it would be for a younger person.

12.12 Contractors and the self-employed

Problems may arise if accident prevention and reporting measures are not communicated to contractors and self-employed persons on site. Arrangements must be made to ensure that contractors and the self-employed are acquainted with, and adhere to, the principal contractor's health and safety standards and procedures, or any other policy or special instructions that may be in force, or relevant to specific operations.

The following recommendations are not exhaustive. Pre-planning at the tender stage may reveal additional requirements.

- Discussion, as necessary, should take place to ensure complete understanding or clarification of what is required.
- A listing of site personnel (who's who and details of established channels of communication).
- The availability, and validity, of certificates and documentation relating to health and safety knowledge and trade competency, including CSCS, CPCS and CISRS cards.
- Safe systems or methods and sequences of work should be established, particularly where such work may affect the health and welfare of others.
- Attention should be given to the requirements for the delivery of plant or equipment, transportation, loading and unloading of materials and provision of means of access; particularly when this work takes place out of normal working hours.

12.13 Supervision and control

The accident trend can be strongly influenced by providing adequate training and supervision to control the worker, the machine or the equipment and the working environment.

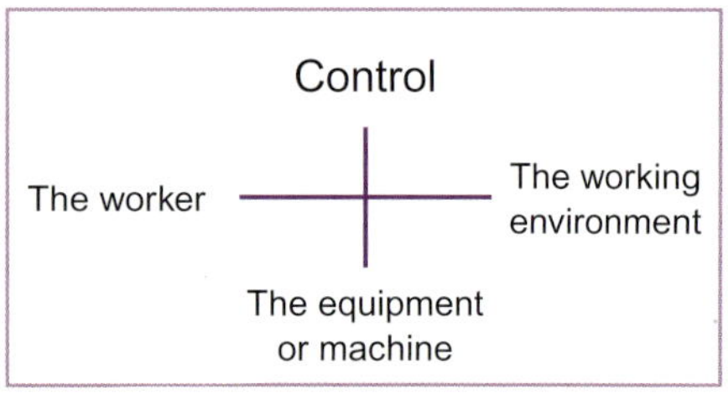

Accident prevention is the control of these factors

12.13.1 The worker

The following points are essential requirements for the worker.

- ☑ Be adequately trained and informed of the work they are expected to do.
- ☑ Be aware of all the hazards in any activity they are expected to do.
- ☑ Competent to do the work or is under adequate suitably qualified supervision.
- ☑ Adopts a safe system of work and uses the protection provided.
- ☑ Be aware of accident and emergency procedures.
- ☑ Be aware of the company's health and safety policy, rules and legislation **applicable to the work**.

12.13.2 The working environment

This applies to all areas of the site, including the work area, stores, offices, depot and welfare facilities.

Regular checks are essential to ensure that these areas remain safe and are not a risk to health.

12.13.3 The equipment or machine

Ensure that the following procedures and practices are observed.

- ☑ Regular inspections are completed by trained and competent persons.
- ☑ No defective equipment is used.
- ☑ Defects are properly rectified.
- ☑ Adequate servicing and maintenance is carried out.
- ☑ Records and reports are maintained.
- ☑ All moving parts are adequately guarded or protected.
- ☑ Manufacturers' literature and instructions are available for operatives.
- ☑ Proper handling, lifting and slinging of equipment is conducted.
- ☑ Equipment and machines are adequately secured, both when in use and parked.
- ☑ Hand tools are inspected and maintained.

For further guidance refer to Chapter A10 Inspections and audits.

Appendix A – Injuries within construction – HSE statistics 2013-14

Kinds of fatal injury in construction

Kind of injury	Fatal injuries 2013-14	Percentage of total fatal injuries to workers in construction
Fall from height.	19	45%
Contact with machinery.	3	7%
Struck by object.	3	7%
Struck by moving vehicle.	3	7%
Contact with electricity.	3	7%
Struck against.	1	2%
Slip, trip or fall on same level.	1	2%
Trapped by something collapsing.	1	2%

Kinds of major and specified injury in construction

Kind of injury to employees	Major or specified injuries in construction 2013-14	Percentage of total major or specified injuries in construction
Fall from height.	581	31%
Slip, trip or fall on same level.	520	27%
Struck by object.	250	13%
Lifting and handling injuries.	170	9%

Kinds of over seven-day injury in construction

Kind of injury to employees	Over seven-day injuries 2013-14	Percentage of over seven-day injuries in construction
Lifting and handling injuries.	992	30%
Slip, trip and fall on same level.	681	21%
Fall from height.	373	11%
Struck by object.	364	11%

www.

For further information refer to the HSE document *Health and safety in construction in Great Britain, 2014*.

13

Accident reporting and investigation

Contents

Supporting information

G: Checklists and forms

GT 700 Toolbox talks

Overview

The recording of incidents and accidents at work is important, to help establish what went wrong, in order to prevent similar incidents and accidents from recurring.

This chapter outlines why and how details of incidents and accidents should be captured, what has to be reported to the Health and Safety Executive (HSE) and how to conduct an investigation.

13.1 Introduction

It may be said that there is no such thing as an accident and without people there are no accidents. An accident can always be put down to human error and it is by no means always the fault of the injured person.

In fact, the HSE considers that a lack of safety management, or procedures, is a contributory factor in a high percentage of accidents, particularly within construction.

The reporting of certain types of accident is a legal requirement and failure to comply is a criminal offence. The reports that are made allow the HSE to identify accident trends, and to take remedial action by producing additional health and safety guidance and legislation, where it is thought necessary.

If you are an employer, self-employed or are in charge of work operations, you have duties under the law. You have to report deaths, specified injuries, non-fatal accidents requiring hospital treatment to non-workers and dangerous occurrences immediately and the HSE should be in receipt of a report within 10 days of the incident. Accidents resulting in over seven-day injuries have to be notified to the HSE within 15 days of the incident. Occupational diseases should be reported as soon as the employer receives the diagnosis.

13.2 Important points

- ☑ It is important that all workplace accidents, no matter how minor, are reported to the injured person's employer, site manager or supervisor as appropriate.
- ☑ There is a legal requirement for details of all accidents to be recorded.
- ☑ Once completed, the record of an accident is subject to the Data Protection Act and is confidential.
- ☑ Certain types of accident, cases of occupational diseases and some dangerous occurrences, must be reported to the HSE.
- ☑ Each company or organisation should have a procedure for investigating workplace accidents.
- ☑ The investigation of accidents will enable trends to be established and preventative measures put in place.
- ☑ The level of investigation should be proportionate to the seriousness of the accident.

13.3 Reporting of Injuries, Diseases and Dangerous Occurrences Regulations

The Reporting of Injuries, Diseases and Dangerous Occurrences Regulations (RIDDOR) requires the following to be reported directly to the appropriate enforcing authority (either the nearest HSE office or the Local Authority).

- ☑ Deaths and specified injuries.
- ☑ Over seven-day injuries.
- ☑ Specified occupational diseases.
- ☑ Dangerous occurrences.

In October 2013 the classification of major injuries to workers was replaced with a shorter list of specified injuries.

The regulations place a duty on the responsible person to make reports to the enforcing authorities. In the case of injuries to employees, the responsible person will be the employer. In the case of the victim being self-employed or a member of the public, the responsible person will be the person in control of the site where the event occurred.

All sub-contractors must notify both the enforcing authority and the main/principal contractor of any reportable accidents.

Where an accident, occupational disease or dangerous occurrence takes place that requires reporting under RIDDOR, a report should be made online via the HSE website.

- ☑ F2508 Report of an injury.
- ☑ F2508 Report of a dangerous occurrence.
- ☑ F2508A Report of a case of disease.
- ☑ F2508G1 Report of a flammable gas incident.
- ☑ F2508G2 Report of a dangerous gas fitting.

The following must be reported immediately to the appropriate authority by the quickest practical method. All incidents can be reported online but a telephone service remains for reporting fatal and specified injuries only. The report must be submitted on the approved form within **10 days**.

- ☑ Death of any person as a result of an accident at work.
- ☑ An accident to any person at work resulting in specified injuries or serious conditions specified in the regulations.
- ☑ Any one of the dangerous occurrences listed in Schedule 2 of the regulations.
- ☑ Non-fatal accidents requiring hospital treatment to non-workers.

A 13

Over seven-day injuries must be reported on an approved form within **15 days**.

For an example of an F2508 form refer to Appendix A.

13.3.1 Why report and record?

The report informs the enforcing authorities (the HSE, Local Authorities and Office of Rail Regulation (ORR), where relevant) about deaths, injuries, occupational diseases and dangerous occurrences, so they can identify where and how risks arise and whether they need to be investigated. This allows the HSE, Local Authorities and ORR to target their work and provide advice about how to avoid work related deaths, injuries, ill health and accidental loss.

Records of incidents covered by RIDDOR are important. They ensure that you collect the minimum amount of information to allow you to check that you are doing enough to ensure safety and prevent occupational diseases. This information is a valuable management tool that can be used as an aid to risk assessment, helping to develop solutions to potential risks. In this way, records also help to prevent injuries and ill health, and control costs from accidental loss.

13.3.2 What must be reported?

13.3.2.1 Work related accidents

Reportable injuries (including deaths) must be reported if they occur as the result of a work related accident and the type of injury is reportable, as listed under types of reportable injuries. For the purposes of RIDDOR an accident is a separate, identifiable, unintended incident that causes physical injury. This specifically includes acts of non-consensual violence to people at work.

When deciding if the accident that led to the death or injury is work related, the key issues to consider are whether the accident was related to the following.

- ☑ The way in which the work was carried out.
- ☑ Any machinery, plant, substances or equipment used for work.
- ☑ The condition of the site or premises where the accident happened.

If any of the above factors were related to the cause of the accident, then it is likely that it will need to be reported to the enforcing authority as a reportable injury. If none of the above factors are satisfied, it is likely that you will not be required to send a report.

Guidance and examples of incidents that do and do not have to be reported are available on the RIDDOR section of the HSE website.

13.3.2.2 Deaths

A death to workers and non-workers must be reported if it results from a work accident or an act of physical violence to the worker.

Where an employee, as a result of an accident at work, has suffered a reportable injury that has caused their death, within one year of the date of that accident, the employer shall inform the relevant enforcing authority, in an appropriate manner, of the death as soon as it comes to their knowledge.

13.3.2.3 Injuries to people at work

RIDDOR gives two types of injury that must be reported if the person was at work – specified injuries and over seven-day injuries.

Specified injuries include the following.

- ☑ A fracture, other than to fingers, thumbs and toes.
- ☑ Amputation of an arm, hand, finger, thumb, leg, foot or toe.
- ☑ Permanent loss of sight or a reduction of sight. Diagnosed by Doctor
- ☑ Any other injury arising from working in an enclosed space leading to hypothermia, heat-induced illness, resuscitation or admittance to hospital for more than 24 hours.
- ☑ Unconsciousness caused by asphyxia or head injury.
- ☑ Crush injuries leading to internal organ damage.
- ☑ Serious burns (covering more than 10% of the body or damaging the eyes, respiratory system or other vital organs).
- ☑ Scalping (a separation of the skin from the head) requiring hospital treatment.

Over seven-day injuries are where an employee, or self-employed person, is away from work or unable to perform their normal work duties for more than seven consecutive days (not counting the day of the accident).

13.3.2.4 Injuries to non-workers

You must report injuries to members of the public or people who are not at work, if they are injured through a work related accident and are taken from the scene of the accident to hospital for treatment to that injury. Examinations and diagnostic tests do not constitute treatment in such circumstances and there is no need to report incidents where people are taken to hospital purely as a precaution when no injury is apparent.

13.3.2.5 Reportable occupational diseases

Employers and self-employed people must report diagnosis of certain occupational diseases (such as those listed below), where these are likely to have been caused or made worse by their work.

- ☑ Hand-arm vibration syndrome (due to operating hand-held vibrating tools and equipment).
- ☑ Occupational dermatitis, due to work substances (such as cement, solvents, epoxy resins).
- ☑ Carpal tunnel syndrome.
- ☑ Severe cramp of the hand or forearm.
- ☑ Tendonitis or tenosynovitis of the hand or forearm.
- ☑ Any occupational cancer (such as mesothelioma, asbestosis (due to work with or exposure to asbestos) and lung cancer).
- ☑ Occupational asthma, where the person's work involves significant or regular exposure to a known respiratory sensitiser.

Occupational deafness is not reportable under the list of occupational diseases, as it is hard to prove the cause of acquired hearing loss (deafness); for example, it could have been caused by any past work activity with exposure to high levels of noise, or through noisy hobbies undertaken outside of the working day.

13.3.2.6 Reportable dangerous occurrences

Dangerous occurrences are certain, listed, near-miss events. Not every near-miss event must be reported. There are 27 categories of dangerous occurrences that are relevant to all workplaces. Some examples are shown below.

- ☑ The collapse, overturning or failure of load-bearing parts of lifts and lifting equipment.
- ☑ Plant or equipment coming into contact with overhead power lines.
- ☑ The accidental release of any substance that could cause personal injury, other than through combustion and flammable liquid or gases.

www.

A full list of dangerous occurrences applicable to all workplaces, and additional categories of dangerous occurrences, can be found on the RIDDOR section of the HSE website.

13.3.2.7 Reportable gas incidents

If you are a distributor, filler, importer or supplier of flammable gas and you learn, either directly or indirectly, that someone has died, lost consciousness or been taken to hospital for treatment to an injury arising in connection with the gas you distributed, filled, imported or supplied, this can be reported online.

If you are a gas engineer, registered with the Gas Safe register, you must provide details of any gas appliances or fittings that you consider to be dangerous to the extent that people could die or suffer a specified injury. This may be due to the design, construction, installation, modification or servicing, and could result in the following.

- ☑ An accidental leakage of gas.
- ☑ Inadequate combustion of gas.
- ☑ Inadequate removal of products of the combustion of gas.

Some examples to provide clarification

- A directly employed person breaks their arm at work. This must be reported by the employer, in their capacity as a responsible person, as a specified injury.
- A self-employed sub-contractor breaks their leg at work. The injury must be reported as a specified injury by the main/principal contractor acting in their capacity as the responsible person who was in control of the premises.
- An employee of a sub-contractor is informed by their doctor that they are suffering from work-related vibration white finger and subsequently informs their employer. The employer, in their capacity as responsible person, must report the incident to the HSE as a reportable disease.
- An employee inadvertently hits an underground electric cable whilst operating a road-breaker. There is minor damage to the external sheath, but the conductor is not exposed. This is not reportable as there was not an electrical short circuit with fire and explosion. The incident, however, warrants significant internal investigation.
- A member of the public is knocked down by a lorry entering the site as it crosses the pavement. They are taken to hospital by ambulance and it is obvious they have suffered an injury. This would be reportable as it involves a member of the public being taken to hospital.
- A sub-contracted employee burns their hand and is taken to the Accident and Emergency Department of the local hospital. The employee is back on site later that afternoon and continues to work as normal for the rest of the week. This would not be reportable. However, had the employee suffered more than 10% burns, the incident would be reportable.
- An employed delivery driver twists their ankle when they step down from their cab. They receive first aid, insist they are fit to drive and later leave the site. They subsequently take the following seven days off because of pain and swelling in their ankle. The incident should have been recorded in the site accident book, but it would seem unreasonable for the site to be aware of the consequence. The delivery driver's employer would have a responsibility to report this as an over seven-day accident.
- An employee sustains a head injury as a result of falling over debris left on site. The accident occurred on a Friday and because of the injury, the person is unable to return to work until a week later on the following Monday. Although only five actual working days have been lost, the accident must be reported as an over seven-day accident because the Saturday and Sunday also count, as the injured person would have been unfit for work had these been working days.

13.3.3 How to report

Complete the appropriate online form, available from the HSE website.

All incidents can be reported online but a telephone service remains through the Incident Contact Centre for reporting fatal and specified injuries only.

13.3.4 Reporting out of hours

The HSE has an out of hours duty officer for circumstances where the HSE may need to respond, which could include the situations shown below.

- Work related death or situation where there is a strong likelihood of death following an incident at, or connected with, work.
- Serious accident at a workplace where there have been multiple injuries.
- Major incident at a workplace where the severity of the incident causes major disruption, such as evacuation of people, closure of roads, and large numbers of people going to hospital.

13.4 Accident records

Employers are legally required to keep records of all accidents. These can be stored in any medium, including electronically, as long as printable copies are readily available if required.

You must keep a record of the following.

- **Accident, occupational disease or dangerous occurrence** that requires reporting under RIDDOR.
- Other occupational accident causing injuries that result in a worker being away from work or **incapacitated for more than three consecutive days** (not counting the day of the accident but including any weekends or other rest days). This is a legal requirement if you are an employer under the Social Security (Claims and Payments) Regulations. An accident book entry will suffice.

You do not have to report over three-day injuries, unless the incapacitation period goes on to exceed seven days, but you still have to keep a record of the over three-day injury.

The period of time for an over three-day injury or an over seven-day injury does not include the day of the accident but it does include any weekends or rest days.

The following details must be recorded.

- Full name, address and occupation of the injured person.
- Date and time of the accident.
- Location of the accident.
- Nature of the injury and how it was caused.

Details of an accident should be recorded by the injured person, but can be completed by any employee. However, some employers insist that records are completed by first aiders, which requires a first aider to be available at all times. This is a company operating procedure and is not strictly necessary.

Completion of an accident record does not meet the employer's obligation to report specific accidents and dangerous occurrences to the HSE or Local Authority.

All accident records have had to comply with the Data Protection Act to ensure the confidentiality of entries. The HSE's accident book BL510 enables each accident record to be detached and stored separately when complete, thus maintaining the confidentiality of the injured person's details. All personal information must be kept in confidence, and in a secure location, such as a lockable cabinet.

Accident books designed and produced in-house may still be used in the following circumstances.

- Where all details required by BL510 are recorded.
- If the requirements of the Data Protection Act are met.
- When information recorded electronically can be made readily available in hard copy.

13.5 Calculating the incidence and frequency rates of accidents

From company accident records and other statistics, it is possible to calculate the incidence and frequency rates for accidents at a particular place of work and for the types of injury, severity or duration.

13.5.1 Accident incidence rate (AIR)

The incidence rate is based on the number of accidents, taken over a fixed period (usually 12 months), per 100,000 employees. The formula below is the one most commonly used by UK Government departments to calculate the incidence rate.

$$\text{Incidence rate} = \frac{\text{Number of reported injuries in a 12-month period x 100,000}}{\text{Average number of employees in a year}}$$

If during a 12-month period there were six reportable accidents and during that year the company employed an average of 120 employees, the calculation would be:

$$\frac{6 \times 100{,}000}{120} = 5{,}000$$

13.5.2 Accident frequency rate (AFR)

The accident frequency rate allows a calculation to be made that balances the number of reportable accidents that occur against the number of hours worked in a fixed period (usually 12 months).

$$\text{Frequency rate} = \frac{\text{Number of accidents in a 12-month period x 100,000}}{\text{Number of hours worked in that period}}$$

If a company had six reportable injuries in a period during which its 120 workers worked a total of 280,000 hours, the accident frequency rate would be:

$$\frac{6 \times 100{,}000}{280{,}000} = 2.14$$

It should be noted that the HSE uses a multiplier of 1,000,000 rather than 100,000 in its guidance on the calculation of AFR. Generally the industry uses 100,000. 100,000 working hours at 45 hours per week for 49 weeks per year, represents 45 years' work for one person or 90 years' work for two persons, and so on.

13.5.3 All accident rates

Similarly by using the above incident and frequency calculations, all accident rates (minors, lost time and reportable accidents) can be calculated.

Computers are ideal for calculating the various incidence and frequency rates, moving averages, and so on. There are many commercially available computer programmes to manage accident statistics or a simple computer programme can be easily devised, using the known labour resources and their total working hours as a basis for calculating the statistics.

To visualise trends more clearly, accident statistics are often displayed as bar charts, histograms and graphs.

The proper and effective reporting of accidents, along with their thorough investigation, can have major benefits for a company. An employer might consider that they could:

- ☑ reduce costs by pro-actively implementing change and preventing accidents
- ☑ identify training needs, which will also improve performance
- ☑ satisfy clients and principal contractors that the workforce is properly trained and totally safety orientated
- ☑ benefit from a possible reduction of insurance premiums following years of hard work to reduce accidents.

13.6 Accident investigation

An effective investigation will meet the following criteria.

- ☑ Be factual and without bias.
- ☑ Clearly show the sequence of events leading to the accident or incident.
- ☑ Identify the immediate cause and the underlying cause (for example, unsafe acts or conditions).
- ☑ Show the root cause (for example, lack of supervision, training or monitoring).

By discovering all causes, especially root causes, you will be able to learn from accidents and incidents and then aim to prevent reoccurrences.

13.6.1 Accident procedure

Many firms have established procedures to be followed in the event of an accident. The procedure below is given as general guidance and outlines the steps that should be taken immediately after an accident.

1.	Attend to the injured person. Call for assistance and arrange for first aid, doctor, ambulance or hospital, as necessary.
2.	Isolate machine, tools or equipment.
3.	Do not disturb or move anything unless to release an injured person.
4.	Inform the manager, safety adviser, safety representative and other appropriate persons (such as the HSE, fire officers, engineers or insurers).
5.	Ensure any remaining hazard is guarded against.
6.	Take notice of anything significant and make general observations at the scene of the accident.

13.6.2 Conducting an investigation

It is not usually practical to investigate every minor accident, but those involving major or serious injuries to persons and major damage to plant or equipment should be thoroughly investigated so that immediate action can be taken to prevent a recurrence. The following headings may be useful as a guide to the steps to be taken.

- ☑ Investigate promptly and record evidence.
- ☑ Identify types of evidence (for example, factual or corroborative).
- ☑ Interview the injured person, if possible.
- ☑ Question the person in charge and other supervisors.
- ☑ Obtain details of the injured person's job and what they usually do.
- ☑ Interview witnesses.
- ☑ Inspect plant for signs of misuse or defects.
- ☑ Establish the full sequence of events.
- ☑ Ascertain the nature and extent of the injury or damage.
- ☑ Complete the accident report and the accident book.
- ☑ Notify the appropriate authorities.

13.6.3 Investigating promptly

The sooner an investigation is started, the better – provided it is safe to do so. Engineers and supervisors will be anxious to find ways and means of repairing any damage to plant, machinery or buildings, but the **first priority** should be to establish the cause of the accident. Safety specialists, managers and safety representatives should concern themselves solely with the safety implications and preventing a recurrence. It is important that the investigation is properly supervised and organised. Where the police or HSE inspectors wish to investigate, any other persons responsible for or involved in investigating the accident must take care not to disturb possible evidence at the scene.

13.6.4 Recording evidence

Statements from witnesses should contain such details as their age and occupation. The time, date and place of interview should be indicated at the end of the statement. Witnesses' statements should always be written in their own words, even if these include slang or expletives.

The completed statement should be read to the witness and, ideally, signed by them and by the person who took the statement.

13.6.5 Identifying the types of evidence

The following will usually be included within evidence.

- ☑ Statement of witnesses and others given orally, or in writing. 'Others' may include experts who, for example, might have been called in to examine a machine or the state of a scaffold.
- ☑ Documentation of all kinds.
- ☑ Material exhibits of all kinds.

13.6.5.1 Factual evidence

Factual evidence comprises the facts related by persons directly involved, and by witnesses who are able to say what they felt, saw, heard, or give an expert opinion. This type of evidence is primary, direct and positive and should be written in simple language, keeping to the facts and avoiding inferences, opinions and beliefs. The facts should be recorded clearly, accurately and in sequence.

The best witnesses are those persons directly involved, who have the following qualities.

- ☑ Can listen carefully to the questions.
- ☑ Are able to answer directly, fairly, impartially and truthfully.
- ☑ Can state clearly when they do not know the answer.
- ☑ Are able to remain calm when they are being asked questions.

13.6.5.2 Material evidence

Material evidence includes, for example, items of plant, equipment, machines, scaffolds, ladders or hand tools, where the use of, or the state or condition of, the item has a bearing on the accident.

13.6.5.3 Corroborative evidence

Corroborative evidence tends to support the truthfulness and accuracy of the evidence that has already been given. The confirming evidence may take the form of site records, plant or maintenance records, warning notices, written procedures or reports made by safety officers or safety representatives.

13.6.5.4 Opinions

Opinions are not generally acceptable as evidence in a court of law, but people in the vicinity of an accident should be asked to give an opinion. In this way a full picture can be built up of the circumstances of the accident.

Experts, or specialists, who are familiar with the type of accident, or technical and other factors surrounding the accident, may be called upon to express their **expert** opinions. When there is a lack of real or factual evidence, other forms of evidence (such as circumstantial and corroborative evidence) tend to become more valuable.

13.6.5.5 Photographs

Photographs taken immediately after an accident record the state of the scene and often highlight conditions that existed at the time. Machines, equipment, tools and obstructions, and factors such as floor conditions, space and dimensions, may show up very well on photographs.

Time, date and place or subject photographed should be written on the back of the pictures.

Too many photographs are far better than too few, and it is a good idea to make drawings of the area where the incident happened. Digital photography may not be accepted as primary evidence but may be suitable as supportive evidence.

Procedures should be in place to ensure that photographs have not been, or cannot be, computer-enhanced, as this would destroy their value as evidence.

13.6.6 Interviewing the injured person

This depends on whether or not the police or the HSE will be involved.

Interviewing the injured person should be an early priority. Even the briefest description of the accident should suffice initially.

The physical and mental state of the injured person will need to be considered, and tact and patience will be required during the interview. The injured person should be fit to answer questions.

The injured person should be encouraged to talk about how the accident happened and it is important they have confidence and trust in the listener. It is important to stress that the purpose of the investigation is to find the cause so that preventive action can be taken. Blame should not be apportioned.

Questioning should not take the form of an interrogation. Someone well known to the injured person is probably the best person to do this. Safety officials are more likely to receive the co-operation of an injured person if they are able to demonstrate a genuine interest in their welfare and recovery. This may involve visiting the injured person, with the doctor's approval, in hospital or at home.

Given the nature of the industry, often with multiple layers of sub-contracting, there may be a number of interested parties. Sharing statements is one way of reducing the stress on witnesses. However, regulators (such as the police and HSE) may be less forthcoming about such arrangements as they may see this as an employer trying to interfere in a criminal investigation.

13.6.7 Questioning the person in charge

Establish from the injured person, manager, supervisor or the person in charge, what the normal job and tasks of the injured person were. Did they include the activity that led up to the accident?

Other questions that might be asked

- ☑ What task or type of job was being performed?
- ☑ Was it planned or part of a planned activity?
- ☑ At what stage of the work did the accident occur?
- ☑ Was the person involved trained and authorised and, if so, when?
- ☑ Was the person authorised to be where the accident occurred?
- ☑ What instructions had been given?
- ☑ Were safe and correct procedures being observed?
- ☑ Did unsafe acts cause the accident? If so, were they those of the injured person, workmates or others?
- ☑ Did any unsafe conditions contribute to the accident?
- ☑ What safety equipment or personal protection was available and in use?

13.6.8 Interviewing witnesses

Skill is required when interviewing. Witnesses should be interviewed one at a time. If they wish to say anything before notes are taken, they should be allowed to do so.

Basic questions interviewers should seek answers to

- ☑ What did the witness actually see or hear?
- ☑ What was the witness doing at the time?
- ☑ What was the proximity of the witness to the accident or occurrence?
- ☑ What actions did the witness take?
- ☑ What actions did others take before and after the accident?
- ☑ What was the condition of the workplace at the time?
- ☑ What hazards or unsafe conditions existed and what unsafe acts were performed?
- ☑ What was the probable cause(s) of the accident or occurrence?

Skilled interviewers allow witnesses to tell things in their own way, intervening only to clear up specific points or answers where necessary. Questions should be impartial and should be recorded together with the answers.

It is quite acceptable to go through an incident with a witness making rough notes and then to take a statement after that. That way, the witness often has more chance to remember and sometimes provides far more detail on the second run through.

The important witnesses are those persons involved. Their evidence will be more valuable than evidence from witnesses who saw or heard only from a distance, although they, too, should be interviewed. Corroborative evidence and information is often required, particularly when witnesses are few or are not reliable.

As much evidence and information as possible should be collected, since the action taken to prevent a recurrence will be based on what is learned.

13.6.9 Inspecting plant for misuse or defects

Inspection of plant, equipment, tools and machinery immediately after an accident may reveal signs of misuse, or defects, which may or may not have contributed to the accident. The scene should also be carefully examined to see if trip hazards, slippery floors, or some other defect contributed to, or caused, the accident.

Assistance from specialists and persons directly involved or familiar with the type of plant, equipment, or machinery in question can provide valuable information.

13.6.10 Establishing a sequence of events

Evidence gained from interviews and from inspection of the scene, plant, equipment or machinery, should give an indication of the sequence of events leading up to the accident.

13.6.11 Ascertaining the extent of injury or damage

It is not always possible to ascertain the full extent of injuries and damage resulting from an accident.

There may be complications or delayed effects from injuries. The total time off work will obviously not be known at the time of investigation.

Whilst it may be easy to identify the extent of the damage caused to plant, machinery, equipment, buildings and materials, it is far from easy to measure the overall effects of the accident in terms of lost time, lost production and, of course, the suffering of the injured person or persons.

13.6.12 Completing the accident investigation report

Accident report details will vary, depending on who produces the report and whom the report is for. To help eliminate or reduce this variation, guidance in making reports and the use of a standard form is recommended.

As far as possible, reports should be concise, based upon fact rather than speculation, be unbiased and should summarise the essential information obtained during the investigation.

It is becoming relatively common for HSE inspectors to simply ask for a copy of an accident investigation report completed by the employer. It could be a criminal offence to manipulate the findings of the report and it is therefore very important to make sure that it is unbiased and, as far as possible, accurate.

Appendix A – Form F2508 Reporting of an injury or dangerous occurrence

HSE Health & Safety Executive

Health and Safety at Work etc Act 1974 ?

The Reporting of Injuries, Diseases and Dangerous Occurrences Regulations 1995

Click here for report guidance

Report of an injury or dangerous occurrence

Filling in this form

This form must be filled in by an employer or other responsible person.

Part A

About you

1 What is your full name?

2 What is your job title?

3 What is your telephone number?

About your organisation

4 What is the name of your organisation?

5 What is its address and postcode?

6 What type of work does the organisation do?

Part B

About the incident

1 On what date did the incident happen?

2 At what time did the incident happen?
(Please use the 24-hour clock eg 0600)

3 Did the incident happen at the above address?

Yes ☐ Go to question 4

No ☐ Where did the incident happen?

☐ elsewhere in your organisation – give the name, address and postcode

☐ at someone else's premises – give the name, address and postcode

☐ in a public place – give details of where it happened

If you do not know the postcode, what is the name of the local authority?

4 In which department, or where on the premises, did the incident happen?

F2508 (05.00)

Part C

About the injured person

If you are reporting a dangerous occurrence, go to Part F. If more than one person was injured in the same incident, please attach the details asked for in Part C and Part D for each injured person.

1 What is their full name?

2 What is their home address and postcode?

3 What is their home phone number?

4 How old are they?

5 Are they

☐ male?

☐ female?

6 What is their job title?

7 Was the injured person (tick only one box)

☐ one of your employees?

☐ on a training scheme? Give details:

☐ on work experience?

☐ employed by someone else? Give details of the employer:

☐ self-employed and at work?

☐ a member of the public?

Part D

About the injury

1 What was the injury? (eg fracture, laceration)

2 What part of the body was injured?

Next Page

A 13

3 Was the injury (tick the one box that applies)

- [ ] a fatality?
- [ ] a major injury or condition? (see accompanying notes)
- [ ] an injury to an employee or self-employed person which prevented them doing their normal work for more than 3 days?
- [ ] an injury to a member of the public which meant they had to be taken from the scene of the accident to a hospital for treatment?

4 Did the injured person (tick all the boxes that apply)

- [ ] become unconscious?
- [ ] need resuscitation?
- [ ] remain in hospital for more than 24 hours?
- [ ] none of the above.

Part E

About the kind of accident

Please tick the one box that best describes what happened, then go to Part G.

- [ ] Contact with moving machinery or material being machined
- [ ] Hit by a moving, flying or falling object
- [ ] Hit by a moving vehicle
- [ ] Hit something fixed or stationary

- [ ] Injured while handling, lifting or carrying
- [ ] Slipped, tripped or fell on the same level
- [ ] Fell from a height

How high was the fall?

[   ] metres

- [ ] Trapped by something collapsing

- [ ] Drowned or asphyxiated
- [ ] Exposed to, or in contact with, a harmful substance
- [ ] Exposed to fire
- [ ] Exposed to an explosion

- [ ] Contact with electricity or an electrical discharge
- [ ] Injured by an animal
- [ ] Physically assaulted by a person

- [ ] Another kind of accident (describe it in Part G)

Part F

Dangerous occurrences

Enter the number of the dangerous occurrence you are reporting. (The numbers are given in the Regulations and in the notes which accompany this form)

Part G

Describing what happened

Give as much detail as you can. For instance

- the name of any substance involved
- the name and type of any machine involved
- the events that led to the incident
- the part played by any people.

If it was a personal injury, give details of what the person was doing. Describe any action that has since been taken to prevent a similar incident. Use a separate piece of paper if you need to.

Part H

Your signature

Signature

Date

If returning by post/fax, please ensure this form is signed, alternatively, if returning by E-Mail, please type your name in the signature box

Where to send the form

Incident Contact Centre, Caerphilly Business Centre, Caerphilly Business Park, Caerphilly, CF83 3GG.
or email to riddor@natbrit.com or fax to 0845 300 99 24

Continue

For official use

Client number	Location number	Event number	
			[ ] INV REP [ ] Y [ ] N

A 13

Index